The Story of Hospital Almoners

The Story of
Hospital Almoners

THE BIRTH OF A PROFESSION

E. Moberly Bell

with a foreword by
Sir Ernest Rock Carling
F.R.C.S., F.R.C.P.

FABER AND FABER
24 Russell Square
London

First published in mcmlxi
by Faber and Faber Limited
24 Russell Square London WC1
Printed in Great Britain by
Latimer Trend & Co Ltd Plymouth

© E. Moberly Bell
1961

Foreword

by Sir Ernest Rock Carling, F.R.C.S., F.R.C.P.

This book appears most opportunely. The almoners' profession is facing a critical moment in its development. Hitherto its field has been predominantly within the hospital, though there have been extensions beyond its walls. It must now restate its scope, range and siting.

The hospital system itself is within sight of considerable change. Treatment without admission, and back to the family doctor, is its aim. In so far as this trend succeeds, the sphere of the almoner too may well move beyond the out-patient department out into the field of general practice and come into closer association with all the external social workers' activities.

If this be so, it is imperative that those planning for the future should know the early history and evolution of the profession. This book deals with the birth of that profession and if it is seen chiefly in the steady progress at one hospital where advances one after another were heralded, that is easily understood.

Those who from the beginning worked elsewhere and had other experience will certainly learn from these pages a great deal that they never knew or had forgotten. A most attractively written book.

February 1960   E. R. C.

Preface

→

This record developed out of a suggestion on
the part of St. Thomas's Hospital that a life of
Anne Cummins should be written. The hospi-
tal most generously placed at my disposal all the almoners'
reports from the foundation of the department to the
present day. Almoners' departments in many other
hospitals, notably St. George's and the Royal Free, have
been equally co-operative.

I have especially to thank Miss A. B. Read of St.
Thomas's Hospital; Miss Cherry Morris and Miss A. S.
MacIntyre who read through the text and corrected me on
various points; Miss K. M. Lewis who gave me informa-
tion on psychiatric social work; Miss M. J. Roxburgh and
Miss M. Steel and the Institute of Almoners; Miss S. Hart
of the Royal Free Hospital and Miss Elinor Lupton of
Leeds.

I have had the pleasure and advantage of meeting some
of those who were in the movement from its earliest days,
Miss W. Locket, who worked at the Royal Free Hospital;
Miss H. Nussey, the first Almoner at Westminster Hospital; Miss L. C. Marx, who worked with Miss Mudd.

The late Mrs. Ramsay, Miss Cummins's secretary for
many years, gave valuable help of a more personal nature
as have also Miss Cummins's kinswoman, Mrs. Buchanan,

9

and her close friend, Miss G. Bompas. Dr. Moorman, Bishop of Ripon, kindly sent me a biographical sketch of his aunt, Miss Gertrude Humpidge.

My thanks are also due to the Family Welfare Association which allowed me access to its earliest records, and especially to Mrs. Torr who was indefatigable in finding material about the effort of the Charity Organization Society to get the work started.

The Family Welfare Association also allowed me to use the portrait of Sir Charles Loch. Of the other illustrations the portrait of Miss Mary Stewart was kindly lent by the Royal Free Hospital; the portrait of Miss Cummins and the group of the Convention by Miss G. Bompas, and the picture of the out-patient department by St. Thomas's Hospital from its archives.

E. M. B.

November 1960

Contents

Contents

Illustrations

———

CHAPTER I

Social Conditions at the End of the Nineteenth Century

'The deserving and undeserving poor.'
BERNARD SHAW

It is always more difficult to understand our immediate predecessors than those of the remote past. This, no doubt, is partly due to the fact that we recognize the necessity of making a real effort of the imagination to recapture the conditions which made witch-hunting and fires at Smithfield possible, while we feel that our grandparents, people whom we have actually seen, ought to look at the world more or less as we do. Yet today this is particularly unreasonable for we are separated from the Victorians by two devastating wars and by revolutions, not only social and political, but also intellectual.

It is a mistake to suppose that the Victorians were smug, self-satisfied hypocrites content with the 'Two Nations' of Disraeli's novel, anxious only for their own material success. On the contrary, it is worth noting that all the social reforms which have built up the Welfare State were initiated by the Victorians and that, not in answer to the pressure of the under-privileged, but through the self-devoted efforts of men and women whose position and wealth would have made it possible for them to ignore the sufferings of the under-dogs.

To appreciate the work of these reformers, it is necessary to understand their conception of the functions of the State, which is entirely different from our own. Tennyson expressed a very general, if not universal, view of society when he wrote of the 'One divine far off event to which the whole creation moves'. The conception was of a beneficent Providence, guiding society to some desirable end. This belief in the forward movement of mankind and society was curiously strengthened by a very common misunderstanding of the theory of evolution. By the less scientifically minded it was believed that the survival of the fittest meant the survival of the best and it followed logically that gradually the good would flourish and all evil perish. This comfortable theory matched very well with the Manchester *laissez-faire* doctrine and in fact led to the view that the function of the State was to hold the ring while the individual made for himself the best life that he could. Fundamentally the social reformers accepted this thesis, but they were not content to leave the weaker and poorer to struggle alone; they did not seek to change the framework of society, but they did do their utmost to help individuals to make as good a life as possible within that framework. The State therefore did little for the welfare of the individual; there were no State schemes for the sick, the unemployed, those who were past work; the only financial relief provided by the tax-payer was through the Poor Law, and this was harsh and meagre. The needy therefore turned to the charitable and there was no real lack of funds; various charities paid out far more annually than the Poor Law Authority spent. There were ancient endowed charities, some dedicated to some particular district or trade, others of a more general character; there were parish charities and in times of unemployment *ad hoc* committees in very many districts for the collection and distribution of funds. And, of course, there was the casual donor, who would always rather give than suffer the discomfort of seeing distress. There was no lack of money or goodwill but since there was no organization, no method in the distribution, the money went not to those whose need was greatest, but to the most plausible. It was to meet this situation that the Charity Organization Society was founded in 1869. The Society was often criticized by those who held that charity and organization go ill together and it was easy for Bernard Shaw and others later to make merry about the 'deserving and undeserving poor', but the principles which inspired the founders of the Charity Organization Society remain sound. No one is served by money indiscriminately given, least of all those who receive it, for no security can be established on the chance generosity of an emotional public.

The Charity Organization Society was in the first place established in London and concerned itself primarily with local charities of all sorts. Among these not the least important were the medical charities. For the sick poor there was no lack of facilities; the Poor Law Authority provided infirmaries, dreaded and disliked by those driven to them, and a rather unsatisfactory medical service in dispensaries; in addition there were Friendly Society clinics and dispensaries. Most important of all, there were the great hospitals. These were all independent foundations, each managed by its own Board of Governors, all staffed by voluntary physicians and surgeons and all supported by voluntary contributions. Many of them were teaching hospitals, and after the establishment of the Medical Register in 1858, their function as schools of medicine became more important and more clearly defined. The reputation of the hospitals was high, and naturally the poor flocked to them.

In the course of time the population of London increased, and with it the demands on the hospitals. The number of patients that could be admitted to the wards was limited by the number of beds and nurses available; it was easy to refuse admission when there was no empty bed. The out-patient department presented a very different problem.

The difficulty had always existed; it was a question both of the choice and of the number of patients who could be admitted. In 1664 we find a complaint at St. Bartholomew's Hospital that 'the apprentices to the three surgeons show pressing importunity and bould saucey carriage to the allmoners to enforce such persons to be admitted as they recommend for the remedy thereof'. In 1678 at the same Hospital the number of out-patients was described as 'burdensome' and it was a burden that became increasingly heavy. Originally, at many hospitals, all applicants for admission, whether to wards or to out-patients' departments, had been interviewed by some of the Governors, and admitted or rejected by them, but the numbers became so great as to make this procedure impossible. In this matter of admitting patients there were four sets of people to be considered and, if

18

possible, satisfied; there were the subscribers to whom 'letters' were given in numbers proportionate to the size of their subscriptions, which entitled them to recommend their protégés for treatment; there was the medical staff, which needed suitable and interesting cases for educational purposes; there were the local general practitioners, who depended for their livelihood on the fees of their patients, and naturally regarded with disfavour the gratuitous treatment of those who should be paying them; and there were, of course, the patients. These last were at once the *raison d'être* of the hospitals and the despair of the administrators, for they came in such quantities. Some indeed were in need of careful diagnosis and treatment, and to some immediate treatment might mean everything. Some were so poor that they needed food rather than medicine; some so ignorant that they barely understood the directions of the doctor, and would much rather have had a bottle of medicine, which could be shared with the family. Some, again, came with trivial indispositions, or merely because they were unemployed and the out-patients' department was less uncomfortable than their homes; while a large number, like the rich who gladly pay a consultant's fees for some quite imaginary illness, came because they dearly loved to discuss their symptoms. The trouble was that there were so many of them, and they were superficially so indistinguishable.

By the time the C.O.S. was founded, the abuse of the out-patients' departments had become notorious and in the following year, 1870, the British Medical Association had begun to concern itself seriously about it. The question was raised by Fairlie Clarke, F.R.C.S., of the Charing Cross Hospital, in a paper read at the Annual Meeting of the B.M.A. on 'The Medical Aspects of Pauperism'. It is worth remarking, because so typical of that age, that he calls for action not only because of the waste of the time of the hospital staff and the impossibility of doing satisfactory work under the conditions prevailing, but also because of the demoralizing effect on patients of receiving gratuitous treatment when they could afford to pay for it. Anxiety on this score was still unallayed at the end of the century, when Loch, General Secretary of the C.O.S., in 1896 in an address to the B.M.A. said: 'We want citizens in our cities, not uncivilized denizens; we want people endowed with foresight, self-supporting and self-respecting. The medical charities, as they are at present administered . . . are helping to thrust a man into the great decadent class to which eventually the word "pauper" is rightly applied.'

Fairlie Clarke's paper roused considerable interest and articles appeared in the medical journals. *The Lancet* indeed expressed the opinion that there could be no abuse of out-patient departments since conditions in them were so appalling, the crowds so intolerable and the treatment necessarily so cursory that no one who could possibly avoid it, would enter such a department. This simple view was, however, refuted by the facts, but the article did something to stimulate efforts to reform the departments. Another result of the paper was the appointment by the C.O.S. of a Medical Sub-committee to deal with the whole question of medical charities. Fairlie Clarke himself became secretary of this committee. In 1875 an appointment of great importance was made at the C.O.S. Charles Loch, a young man who was at that time in the secretarial office of the British Medical Association, became the General Secretary of the Society; from that time he was the moving spirit in the fight for the reform of medical charities in general and the out-patient departments in particular. He worked tirelessly and with complete devotion; his perseverance was quite remarkable and those who study the records cannot fail to be struck by the melancholy fact that in 1888 he was reiterating the things he had said persistently in 1875. But in 1888 he prefixes his report with the words, 'The old evils remain with regard to Out-patient Departments'.

In 1875 things had looked more promising. Four years earlier there had been a very well-attended conference in which all the London Hospitals and dispensaries had agreed to make a concerted effort to promote Provident Dispensaries. This was to enable patients to maintain their self-respect by paying, while they were in health and in work, a small weekly sum which would entitle them to free treatment in times of need. The hospitals agreed that they would not treat those who could, but would not, subscribe. Unfortunately this scheme, which should have done so well, failed because it seemed quite impossible to discriminate between those who lacked the means and those who lacked the self-respect; and those who began with the self-respect were apt to waver when they saw their less worthy neighbours getting the same treatment gratuitously.

Fairlie Clarke entered the fray again. In an article in *Macmillan's Magazine*, entitled 'Hospital Reform' (August, 1874), he put the case and suggested the remedy. 'The proper clients for a hospital may be easily defined in general terms. They are those who are raised above the level of pauperism but who are not able to pay even the

21

lowest scale of medical charges. I admit that it is not always easy to say in the case of a particular individual, whether he does or does not belong to this section. . . . How then are we to discriminate between those who are and who are not proper subjects for gratuitous medical charity? Surely such an important duty ought not to be entrusted to the Hall Porter?' He goes on to suggest the appointment of a responsible officer to be charged with the duty of making the enquiries necessary for discriminating and he gives an interesting summary of the qualities such an officer should possess. 'He should be altogether raised above the class of the applicants; he should be a man of some education and refinement, of a kind and forbearing disposition, but at the same time possessed of firmness and discrimination of character and tact and should be thoroughly acquainted with the neighbourhood and with all the charities in the surrounding parishes.' He foresaw that the problem of finding money to pay for this paragon might be a serious deterrent to trying the experiment, but he argued that in the end the appointment of such an officer would be a good investment. This article was followed by discussions and conferences, and the hospitals were moved to take up the question seriously.

The first to act was the Westminster, which appointed a Committee to enquire into the out-patients' department because the number of patients had become unmanageable; the Committee met and made a report recommending the abolition of 'letters' from subscribers as well as the elimination of unsuitable applicants. The report was adopted, but no action followed. The Royal Free Hospital was the next; it asked the C.O.S. to make an enquiry into the circumstances of its out-patients; the enquiry was made and it was estimated that rather less than 30 per cent of the applicants were suitable cases and nearly 40 per cent were able to join a Provident Dispensary. These figures were noted but no action was taken. The Hospital for Sick Children, Great Ormond Street, next offered, but there, as soon as the applicants discovered that an inquiry was to be made into their circumstances, they faded away, and the hospital found itself actually short of patients.

These efforts belong to the 70's. In the 80's many hospitals found themselves in financial difficulties, and this once more raised the question of the possibility of excluding from hospitals those who were able, but unwilling, to pay anything towards the cost of their treatment. Accordingly, more than one hospital invited Loch to institute inquiries into the incomes of their patients. It is recorded in 1886 that 406 visits had been made to 71 hospitals for this purpose, but the inquiries proved very unpopular, though, we are assured, they were made 'with the greatest delicacy and care'. Many surgeons complained that as a result, they were losing many of their most interesting patients. The inquiries therefore were dropped. 'All this', reported the Secretary of the Medical Committee of the C.O.S., 'proves that hospitals are aware of the need for reform, but fear to adopt measures of too radical a cure, lest they should render their hospitals odious to their clients'. That was the crux. In general terms all agreed that reform was necessary—urgent even —but as soon as it touched any particular hospital, or affected any individual, more especially if it seemed to be unpopular, then it was stigmatized as ill-conceived and worse, unworthy of execution.

23

In 1888 the Committee of the Charity Organization Society came to a definite conclusion: 'So great is the disinclination to change . . . that it would seem only the investigation of a Royal Commission would thoroughly sift the subject and propose reforms, with the consideration and authority necessary to their gradual acceptance by the public and the medical profession.' To the task of securing some sort of public inquiry Loch now gave his attention. The Charity Organization Society had influential friends and it took only three years to secure this. In 1891, just twenty years after the struggle for reform had begun, a Select Committee of the House of Lords was appointed to inquire into 'the position and the finances of Metropolitan Hospitals'. The Committee met and proceeded to the examination of a great many witnesses. Loch was called, and his evidence was based on the experience of twenty years' consideration of the evils of the existing system of medical relief. What impression his evidence made we have no means of knowing. The Commission, after the manner of Parliamentary Commissions, deliberated long and finally, some three years after its appointment, produced recommendations, of which the most important were the appointment of a central body to supervise the London Hospitals and the establishment of a common system of accounts in all these hospitals. These recommendations were implemented indeed, but not until the National Health Act of 1948, and thus had no importance for the out-patients of the nineteenth century. Charles Loch had not been unduly hopeful of any concrete help from the Commission and he had not waited for the publication of its findings. He had continued to pursue his own object—the appointment of social workers to deal with out-patient departments. He had already established relations of confidence with G. F. Sheppard of the Royal Free Hospital. This hospital had always been forward-looking; it had taken the bold step of admitting women medical students to its wards in 1877, it had been the first to attempt a serious factual investigation of its out-patients' circumstances; Loch hoped that it would now make the experiment of employing a trained social worker in that department. Sheppard was willing enough but the Hospital Board had to be converted and, as Fairlie Clarke had foreseen, the provision of a salary was a stumbling block. Negotiations were protracted but at last agreement was reached. For an experimental period of three months the hospital was willing to accept the appointment to the out-patients' department, of a trained social worker to be chosen and paid by the C.O.S. Loch was triumphant. The secretary of the North St. Pancras District Office of the C.O.S., Mary Stewart, was sent to the Royal Free Hospital and began her work there in January 1895.

CHAPTER II

Hospital Out-patients

*'The number of out-patients has become burdensome;
not more than 8 are to be admitted in a week.'*
Minute of St. Bartholomew's Hospital Governors,
3rd June 1678

With the appointment of Mary Stewart to the Royal Free Hospital, after a gestation of twenty-five years the new profession was born. Loch was the only begetter and Sheppard the midwife. The child was named; she was called The Lady Almoner. The word 'almoner' has a long history in the language. It appears first in English in the fourteenth century and in its early days was used as the title of that officer whose duty it was to distribute alms to the poor, from the religious at the gate of a monastery, or from royalty at the gate of a palace; later it was a title given to the Governors of the ancient Royal Hospitals of St. Bartholomew and St. Thomas, who undertook to receive all applicants for admission to the hospital and accept or reject them. With the increase in the numbers of applicants this duty had fallen into abeyance, but the title persisted. Since it was hoped that Mary Stewart would perform this work of discrimination, it was logical that the name

'Almoner' should be given her. This was perhaps unfortunate, for the word suggested dealing with money, and though indeed the Almoner had always dispensed rather than collected it, with a confusion of thought not uncharacteristic of us, the Almoner came to be identified by the public with the collection of contributions from those who attended hospital and this had a detrimental effect on her status. For the purpose of distinguishing the new almoner from her august namesakes, the word 'Lady' was prefixed. To modern ears, this title carries implications entirely absent at that date. In 1895 there was no embarrassment in being called a lady; there were lady doctors, lady secretaries, and lady clerks; to add to these a lady almoner seemed sufficiently obvious. So the new-born profession was to be that of the Lady Almoner. But it was at this stage rather a sickly infant and exposed at once to a cold and unfriendly world.

Mary Stewart had for some years been working as Secretary to the North St. Pancras Committee of the Charity Organization Society. She belonged to that generation of Victorian women to whom the opportunity of education had appeared as a glorious adventure. She had come under the influence of Miss Buss of the North London Collegiate School, and not content to live a life of refined penury as a daughter in the home, she had trained under the C.O.S. as a social worker. She came to the Royal Free Hospital therefore with much knowledge of the conditions of the poor and the problems she would be called upon to face. The most difficult of these problems she had probably not anticipated—this was the suspicion and hostility with which most of the medical staff regarded her. Her work had been carefully defined. She

27

was to prevent the abuse of the hospital by those who could afford to pay, to refer those in need of relief to the Poor Law and to recommend all who could afford to do so to join a Provident Dispensary. The doctors, however, made it perfectly clear that the ultimate authority to select or reject applicants was in their hands and not hers. The medical staff certainly wanted the chaos of the out-patient department reduced to order; the doctors resented the time wasted on trivial cases, on patients who wandered from hospital to hospital getting a bottle of medicine here and advice there and profiting by neither; they had clearly no time themselves to discriminate by inquiry into social conditions; something certainly ought to be done. But, to have a woman, not really under their control, in a quasi-official capacity—this was too disconcerting and very much to be deprecated.

This almost instinctive hostility of doctors and surgeons was not peculiar to the Royal Free Hospital. It recurred at every hospital when the first Lady Almoner appeared. In America too, Dr. Cabot, of the Massachusetts General Hospital found exactly the same situation when the work began there. In 1909 he wrote 'Unless there is at least one doctor who really knows what the Social Worker is trying to do, the scheme fails. If he thinks of her merely as a nurse, she will fall short of his expectations. Unless he has already acquired the "social point of view" to the extent of seeing that his treatment of patients is slovenly without some knowledge of their homes, finances, thoughts and worries, he will think that the social worker is trying to teach him how to do his work, whenever she does what he didn't and couldn't do before. Naturally he will resent this indignantly. He will not care to be advised by any "woman charity worker"; that she can throw light on his case implies that his vision was not previously clear. I have seen a good deal of such irritation implied or expressed in the comment of physicians on social work in hospitals and in the long run it is sure to checkmate the effort of the social worker, no matter how tactful she is.'

Mary Stewart seems to have been by disposition tactful and diplomatic. It is difficult to gain any very clear idea of her personality, for there are no letters of hers left and there are few living who knew her intimately, but from those who remember her one gathers that she was a very gentle person, sensitive and compassionate, very conscientious and anxious to fulfil exactly the duties with which she was charged, but deeply conscious that the more important part of the work she was doing consisted, not in protecting the hospital against the fraud of those who would exploit it, but in making it possible for every patient to profit from the time and skill so lavishly bestowed upon him. The office assigned to the almoner at the Royal Free Hospital was a small corner of the out-patient waiting-room partitioned off by screens; there was neither light nor air and if a visitor came in the only seat available was the radiator. Here Mary Stewart began her work. For the first month since no doctor recommended any individual to her, all she could do was to judge by appearances which of the out-patients could most profitably be questioned. In the course of the first month she examined the situation of 150 patients and attempted a classification according to their means. To the Committee of Management she reported that she found no evidence of deliberate fraud, though she believed that many patients could, if they wished to do so, join a Provident Dispensary.

During the next two months, Mary Stewart began in some small degree to overcome the prejudice of some of the staff; two doctors began to send patients to her and she was able to abandon the method of random choice. She tried to interview all new applicants, but made enquiries only of those who seemed able to provide to some extent for their own needs. More and more it seemed to her that many applicants ought to join one of the medical provident dispensaries and she was discouraged to find that most of the applicants had never heard of such an institution. When she told them how desirable it was to make provision in days of health for future needs, they promised to think it over; unfortunately, when they came to think it over, the idea of paying out of a small wage for a hypothetical illness, which, if it came, would be treated gratuitously by the hospital, did not commend itself to them and in spite of all her efforts few joined a dispensary and fewer still persevered in their membership.

This problem of persuading out-patients to join a Provident Dispensary, was one which confronted every almoner in the early days. The movement to establish these institutions, actively supported by the Medical Committee of the C.O.S., by the British Medical Association and by every society concerned with the administration of medical relief, had never commended itself to those whom it was intended to benefit. Wages were small. The English—perhaps not only they—are by nature gamblers; they are prepared to take a chance, to spend their earnings and hope for the best. In vain did one almoner after another exhort her applicants to join a

Dispensary. It was a losing battle. The promoters of these institutions were hoping to induce people to do from a high altruistic motive what could, in fact, only be enforced by the law. Leaseholders are compelled to insure their houses, motorists their cars, but it was not until a series of Insurance Acts, the earliest in 1911, that the workman was compelled to insure his health and a legal demand for payment was substituted for exhortations to thrift. This, at last, eliminated one problem from the work of an almoner.

But if Mary Stewart had had little success in recruiting for the Provident Dispensaries, she had nevertheless managed to convince a majority of the Management and some part at least of the Staff that the work she was doing was of real value and when at the end of her three months' probationary period the question of her re-appointment arose, there was a general, if not very strong, desire to agree to it on the same terms as before. Now, however, a difficulty arose. The C.O.S. had given money to the hospital to enable it to test the value of an almoner. That value had now been proved and since it was a fundamental principle of the C.O.S. not to go on subsidizing those who could support themselves, it now withdrew its contribution to the almoner's salary. The hospital, for its part, wanted an almoner, but not enough to be willing to pay for it. Both sides remained obdurate and Mary Stewart went back to the North St. Pancras office of the C.O.S. So the matter stood for six months, but there were two members of the Medical Committee of the C.O.S. who were not content to leave it so; they believed sufficiently in the value of the work and the importance of proving it beyond all doubt, to back it financially; each gave £25 both to the C.O.S. and to the R.F.H., on condition that an almoner was appointed for a year. This saved the situation; neither C.O.S. nor the Royal Free Hospital was obliged to climb down and Mary Stewart returned to her little black hole in the hospital. With wonderful magnanimity, the hospital made an additional payment of £25 so that she enjoyed a salary of £125 which, for a woman at that date, was not abysmally low. So the work began again. During the years that remained to her at the hospital, Mary Stewart increasingly justified the faith of those who had appointed her; the C.O.S. was asked for no further contribution to her salary and there was no hesitation about continuing the work.

The Hospital Committee noted with pleasure—and some surprise—that there had been no complaints from applicants about the questions put to them by the almoner. To Mary this seemed not at all surprising; experience had taught her that there was little need to ask questions. It is a very general, indeed almost universal, human characteristic to enjoy talking about oneself. Reticence is a quality acquired through education and the gradual perception that one's own affairs are not of paramount interest to one's fellows. But the out-patients had for the most part not acquired this degree of education and it only needed a hint, a friendliness of attitude and an evident readiness to listen, to open the floodgates and all the anxieties, the problems, financial and emotional, were poured forth readily enough. In the Lady Almoner the out-patients saw not an inquisitor, but a friend.

The work increased steadily. In 1897 it was extended to ward patients. There was far more than any one woman could do and the Hospital Committee appointed assistants

1. *A portrait of C. S. Loch of the Charity Organization Society by Sargent*

2. *A portrait of Mary Stewart who was the first lady almoner and was appointed to The Royal Free Hospital in 1895*

3. *The out-patients department at St. Thomas's Hospital at the beginning of the Century*

—notably Miss Brimmell and Miss Davidson—to the office. It was a happy team, for it was not the least of Miss Stewart's qualities that she was easy to work with or under and many voluntary workers came gladly to her aid. This was admirable, but it was impossible to make full use of these volunteers in the restricted space allotted to the almoner's office. Sheppard reported this to the Committee and as a result it was agreed in March 1898 that an effort should be made to improve the accommodation. In the course of the next two years this was accomplished and the almoner's office was rehoused in what at that time appeared to be spacious and convenient quarters.

In 1897 Mary Stewart conceived the idea of making a register of all the applicants to her office. This does not, to us, seem a very revolutionary proposition, indeed it is difficult to imagine any organization of today without some index of its clients. But it was not so then. The voluntary workers began the index and in June 1898 Miss Stewart reported to her Committee, 'It would greatly facilitate the work of identifying patients if the Board could see their way to providing a Card Index for the Almoner's office. The numbers, now upwards of 5,000, have quite outgrown the small book which has been used.' The Board was faintly uneasy about 'A Register', which seemed in some ill-defined manner to give to an almoner authority over patients, but it could not well refuse so modest a request and the card index was conceded. It says much for the competence and zeal of the voluntary workers that by 1899 every entry had been transferred from the 'small book' to the cards.

Unfortunately, by this time Mary Stewart's health began to fail; she had never been very strong and the strain

C   33

of the work, its constant demands on mind and body, the perpetual tension in working with those who must be placated, was beginning to prove too much for her. In the autumn of 1898 she was obliged to ask for leave of absence, readily granted in the hope that she might be able to return to the work. In her absence, various trained or partly trained social workers came to the rescue, but the bulk of the work fell on Miss Brimmell, who had been an assistant for some time, ably helped by Miss Locket, an enthusiastic volunteer. Mary Stewart came back indeed, but it was only to find that she could no longer sustain the work and she resigned and was succeeded by Miss Brimmell.

So ended the work of the first Lady Almoner. Her achievement has perhaps been overshadowed by the greater work done by her successors, but it must never be forgotten that the qualities she brought to her task, her tact, her friendliness and quiet efficiency made the subsequent work possible. It was her devotion to duty, her sympathy with patients and endless forbearance with the medical staff, her absolute blindness to any snub or discourtesy shown to herself that overcame the initial prejudice of the doctors, and saved the infant profession from being strangled at birth.

CHAPTER III

The Beginning of Professional Consciousness

◁━━━▷

'Here is the solution of the whole problem of medical relief.'

C. S. LOCH's letter to *The Times* 1898

The profession had made a start, but the appointment of one almoner to one hospital could do no more than demonstrate the way in which the difficulties presented by overcrowded out-patient departments could be tackled. The whole intricate problem of the proper administration of medical relief remained and was increasingly the concern of the Medical Committee of the Charity Organization Society, the British Medical Association, and the Hospital Saturday Fund. The attitude of the C.O.S. was consistent, being based on a long experience of social work and a definite theory as to the right use of charitable endowments, which should not be thrown away upon those whose economic state would make them permanently dependent and who therefore were proper subjects for Poor Law Relief, but should be used to re-establish those in temporary difficulties. As a means of making this discrimination possible in hospitals, the C.O.S. had no doubt that the appointment of a properly trained almoner to every hospital was an essential and it pointed to Mary Stewart's work as a proof of its contention.

The very general interest of the public in this problem was reflected in the summer of 1898 in a correspondence in *The Times*, in which C. S. Loch described the work being done at the Royal Free Hospital, claiming that here was the solution of the whole problem of medical relief. A Governor of St. Mary's Hospital at once wrote challenging this claim. 'At St. Mary's,' he said, 'an investigation officer was employed; he was a retired policeman, with an intimate knowledge of the district; he was present when all applicants arrived and was able from a long experience to assess their situation, with some shrewdness.' Other correspondents joined in, some advocating an enquiry into all the systems in use, others suggesting that each hospital must work out its own methods and there was no difference in principle between the method in use at the R.F.H. and at St. Mary's. Actually the emphasis was so differently placed in the two systems that it amounted to a difference of principle; the policeman at St. Mary's was concerned primarily to protect the hospital from exploitation by 'unsuitable' cases; the almoner at the Royal Free Hospital to enable the patient to make full use of the skill and time given so freely by the hospital and to see that nothing should be wasted owing to the patient's material or intellectual poverty. The correspondence at least proved that on one point there was general agreement— that some sort of investigation into the needs of applicants was essential. When, in 1898, the Hospital Saturday Fund announced that in making grants to the various hospitals it would be influenced by evidence of discrimination in accepting out-patients, the appointment of some sort of enquiry officer assumed a new importance. Some hospitals were moved to appoint an enquiry officer of the St. Mary's type, others began cautiously to look about for an almoner on the model of the Royal Free Hospital. The Westminster Hospital was among the latter and in 1899 a member of the medical staff asked Miss Spencer of the Central Bureau for the Employment of Women to look round for a suitable person. She advised Helen Nussey to apply for the post, and her appointment as Lady Almoner followed. The thing was done without reference to the C.O.S., who bitterly disapproved. Helen Nussey was young—she was twenty-four to be exact—a year younger than the C.O.S. was prepared to accept candidates for the almoners' training; she had had little training in social work, having done only one day a week for a year with the C.O.S. This seemed to the Society woefully insufficient for so important a post. Miss Nussey herself was convinced that she owed her appointment largely to this very inexperience. The hospital was rather afraid of the step it was taking and did not wish to have anyone who would endeavour to put the staff right. 'I saw a shudder pass over the Committee, when I mentioned the C.O.S.,' she recorded many years later, and when Loch heard that no one with better experience had applied for the job, he relented and arranged for the new almoner to spend some months at the Royal Free Hospital before she took up her appointment.

The House Committee of the Westminster Hospital reported to the Governors that 'with a view to the better organisation and the greater usefulness of the Out Patient

Department,' it had appointed an almoner. No rules were laid down, no restrictions imposed as to the methods by which these objects were to be attained; it was left to the Almoner to work out her own system and make her own plans. There were, as always in this work, two sides to the problem—numbers in the out-patients' department must be reduced by the selection of the right ones to attend; and those attending must be helped to make full use of the facilities offered. This obviously involved visiting, and no one person could possibly get round the necessary work. It was on this account that an agreement had been made with the C.O.S., that any almoner could obtain the help of its workers in paying friendly visits. Helen Nussey, however, remembered the shudder that had shaken the appointing committee at the mention of the Society, and felt therefore inhibited from asking for the help she so greatly needed. However, as the days passed on, she found herself able to consult one of the out-patient doctors whom she felt to be 'neutral' about the C.O.S. and he advised her to ask the Society's help, promising to support her if any question arose. This reduced the volume of her work, though there was plenty still to do. She conceived the work to be primarily that of a liaison officer, both within and without the hospital. It was slow going at first; most members of the staff were inclined to regard with suspicion the idea that anyone could help them in understanding their patients and were inclined to refer to the almoner only such obvious cases as those needing convalescence or surgical appliances; but gradually they came to perceive that she had a knack of finding out things about the patients that it was useful to know and problems of all sorts were referred to her. It was Miss Nussey's concern to establish the fact that any case referred to her, whether by doctor, nurse, or even the porters, was thoroughly investigated. She took pains to see that the outcome of her enquiries was made known to the person who had reported the case. Gradually the staff came to have confidence in her judgment and she found her suggestions frequently adopted by those in authority.

In establishing contacts with those outside the hospital —parish clergy, charities and doctors in private practice— Miss Nussey's first principle was to ensure that the almoner's office should by no one be regarded as another centre for the distribution of relief. She was there to introduce those who really needed material help to agencies founded to meet that need. She was ready to do this, but, like all her contemporaries, she had a horror of fostering improvidence and of relieving people of responsibilities which, with a little sturdiness of character, they could discharge themselves. She had a quite genuine belief that most people would really wish to retain their independence, and she was confirmed in this faith by the number of her clients who accepted her view. Generally after a talk with her in which she made it clear to them that any relief they took came, not as manna from Heaven, but out of someone else's pocket, they were convinced that it was the part of self-respecting people to meet their own expenses and chose to pay, by instalments, for the convalescence or whatever it was they needed rather than to take the money. This is an out-moded attitude, but the fact that so large a proportion of Westminster outpatients adopted it when the almoner put it to them, proves the force of her sincerity and the strength of her influence.

Looking back, long after her retirement, Helen Nussey recalls 'getting things and help for patients was left entirely to me. All the doctors noted was that they did get the things they required and attended more regularly in consequence. Before an almoner was appointed the patients just ceased to attend if they did not know how to get what was advised. After the first six months of having an almoner one of the doctors previously quite unknown to me wrote asking if I would write something in their journal as they all felt the work was very useful. I shall never forget my astonishment, as hitherto I had had no indication of any sort whether they liked it or not.'

This request resulted in a series of self-revealing articles published in the *Westminster Hospital Gazette*— the journal of the medical students—in which she describes some incidents in the life of the 'Lady Harmony', the title by which many of her clients addressed her. She writes amusingly about these clients; sometimes she is caustic; they are always ignorant, sometimes exasperating and very often incompetent. There is the lady who arrives without her card; she cannot remember the name of the doctor she saw, nor how long ago she saw him; she gladly volunteers the name of the disease from which she is suffering, but it is one unknown to medical science. Finally the somewhat exhausted almoner begins a search through all the records and when the table is strewn with case papers and the almoner is wondering rather hopelessly what next she can do, the lady remarks brightly, 'Of course I've been married since I was here last'. There is the patient suffering from 'strong ammonia', the lady who has 'seen better days' and whose gentility is overpowering; there is the tuberculous patient who, being asked if he always remembers the importance of hygienic habits replies with emphasis, 'Lor, yes Miss. I never spits without thinking of you!' Through all the incidents recounted there are two very obvious characteristics displayed by the almoner; the first is her genuine respect for the personality of her clients, she laughs at them, but it is the laughter of a friend. Their essential decency, their honesty, their courage is brought out in one anecdote after another and is all the more convincing because these things are not underlined or sentimentalized. The second quality is the utter lack of pomposity or self-importance of the almoner. With engaging simplicity she records her own misjudgments, her failures as well as her successes and this may be no small part of Helen Nussey's contribution to the establishment of the profession. The medical students who passed from Westminster Hospital to become consultants elsewhere would be very unlikely to think of an almoner as a tiresome hostile critic; they would know something of the value of her work and appreciate the contribution she could make to the hospital she served.

St. George's was the next hospital to venture on the appointment of a woman almoner. The inquiry officer first appointed, a man of no particular education and quite without training, had found himself unable to cope with the work. With some reluctance it was decided that a woman must be tried. Edith Mudd, who was appointed in October 1901 was a very unusual woman and one whose contribution to the profession was of considerable importance and has perhaps been underestimated. She came of a Sussex family, the name was originally Maude. Her father had a practice at Storrington and both her brothers were doctors. It was therefore natural enough that when this new profession, intimately connected with medicine, was being established, she should be interested in it and determine to train for it. But she was not the kind of woman that becomes entirely absorbed in her professional work. She was essentially a countrywoman and her interests were widely diffused; she was deeply learned in country lore, an intrepid mountaineer and gained the distinction of giving her name to a peak in the Alps. She was a diviner of all sorts of minerals as well as of water and it is said that in this last she was never known to fail. She had a fine infectious zest for life which made her a stimulating companion; and a gift for entertaining. Those who still remember her tell of her delightful luncheon parties, her beautiful clothes and her lovely rings. She attacked her work with the greatest gusto, bringing to it something of the spirit of an amateur, in the best sense of that word.

To such a woman work at St. George's was not likely to be very easy. There was no one, like Sheppard at the Royal Free Hospital, who believed steadily in the necessity for an almoner and was determined to make her a success. On the contrary, the Almoner's Committee appointed to take charge of her department was only half reconciled to using a woman, and her chances were not improved by the publication in the *Nursing Times* of the statement that she was 'a lady of independent means'. This might also seem to suggest an independent mind, very unbecoming in a female. However, the appointment having been made, the Committee was willing enough to do what it could to help. It met to formulate the conditions of her work and passed a Resolution affirming that she was to combine investigation of the circumstances of the

out-patients with the giving of relief and for this they
voted her the magnificent sum of £35 for the first year.
Even allowing for the different value of money at that
time, it seems difficult to suppose that this sum would go
very far among the over-numerous applicants in the out-
patients' department. The space assigned to the almoner's
work was cut off by screens from the room in which
patients were put while they came round from anaes-
thetics after operations; it was neither comfortable nor
convenient, but Edith Mudd settled herself in cheerfully.
For the first two months things went reasonably well and
the Almoner's Committee passed a resolution in January,
1902, expressing its appreciation of her work and conveying
its thanks to her. Unfortunately, this halcyon atmosphere
did not last long. In October the Almoner's Committee is
found investigating a complaint against the Almoner from
the Hospital Saturday Fund. The incident is trivial and
ridiculous, but worth recording because it was the turning
point in Edith Mudd's relations with her Committee and
illustrated aptly the difficulties which beset the paths of all
almoners in these early experimental years. The Hospital
Saturday Fund, which only a few years earlier had insisted on the importance of investigation into the finances
of out-patients, now accepted at once the complaint of
three patients, that they had been denied treatment at St.
George's by the almoner because they were earning 30s.
a week. Investigation proved that they had not been refused admission or even relief; all that had in fact happened was that the almoner had inquired into their earnings and had recorded them. As an afterthought one of
the three declared that the almoner had said his ill health
was due to his immorality. This Miss Mudd flatly denied

and no one appears to have taken the allegation very seriously. The Almoner's Committee stood by its officer; it sent a firm reply to the H.S.F. denying the validity of the complaints and setting forth the true facts. But no doubt the Committee was shaken. To fall out with the H.S.F., that source of bounty, was very much to be deprecated. It ought never to have happened and certainly must never happen again. A new Committee was set up to consider afresh the exact limits of the almoner's duty and to make any new regulations that seemed desirable. This Committee decreed that the clerk—presumably the clerk to the Hospital Board—should receive all applicants and enter in a book the particulars of each one, including earnings, and that the almoner should interview only such cases as the clerk referred to her. This plan of course put a very serious responsibility into the hands of the clerk, who had no special qualifications to fit him for it; it prevented Miss Mudd from investigating cases recommended by the C.O.S. or the local clergy, a practice which had worked very satisfactorily, but on the other hand, it did give her time, by reducing the number of cases with which she was concerned, to deal more fully with those referred to her.

She used this time profitably, making full use of the C.O.S. visitors, especially in the maternity cases. The ignorance of these expectant mothers was appalling and Miss Mudd was able to educate them to some small extent in matters of hygiene and diet. Tuberculous patients were also much in need of health education. The idea that fresh air and extra nourishment were the most important elements in curing this disease and the danger of infecting other members of the family, now universally recognized,

were at that time almost entirely unknown to all but the
most advanced and there was much work to do in this
field. Despite earlier complaints, Miss Mudd's relations
with the patients were good; they appreciated her constant good humour and her understanding of their problems; she inspired confidence. She was able therefore to do
real good in this educative work. But when the Almoner's
Committee of St. George's became aware of what was
going on, it was curiously disturbed. That a woman
should attempt any such work was absurd. A serious complaint was formally made that: 'a department, preventing
abuse and furthering convalescent treatment and sanatorium treatment has practically become, without
authority, a health visiting society; the Almoner's Department has taken up a branch of Health Education and
Preventive Work entirely unknown to the Committee.'
Here was a pretty state of affairs! A woman giving advice
(however good) without asking the doctors. This was
intolerable. It is a pity that Edith Mudd was never able to
do for St. George's all the work her great intelligence and
generous devotion might have accomplished. Success in
the field of medical social service depends on co-operation
and mutual understanding between doctor and social
worker, and at St. George's this had never been established. None the less a great deal had been done which
showed the way to those who came after and it was perhaps here, working under Edith Mudd, that Anne Cummins, later so outstanding in this work, came to realize
the immense importance of treading delicately with
medical authority and hospital staff and winning their
confidence; here too she saw the great field that lay open
for an almoner in maternity and tuberculous cases.

By 1903, eight years after the appointment of the first Lady Almoner, seven London Hospitals were employing them. These women had all worked at the Royal Free Hospital at some time or another, they knew one another and naturally had much in common—the same problems to solve, the same difficulties to face. It was Edith Mudd's idea that they should form themselves into a Committee to discuss common difficulties and problems. The first meeting was held at her flat in Artillery Mansions under her chairmanship. It was agreed that they should meet monthly at the R.F.H. and should send Minutes of these meetings to the Medical Committee of the Charity Organization Society, with one of their number to represent them on that Committee. Miss Brimmell was chosen. The almoners found these meetings useful and encouraging. A perennial difficulty was the great diversity among the hospitals in their attitude to out-patients. All proclaimed their desire to reduce the number of these patients but there their unanimity ceased. Each hospital wanted to be popular in its own district and each wanted to secure the most interesting cases for its own medical students. Edith Mudd reported that a patient at St. George's, being asked some question, had replied that they need not bother, 'there are plenty of hospitals not so particular'. Of course this small body of women could not hope to establish a common standard in all London hospitals, but they could at least determine what line they should follow in the hospitals they served. They discussed at great length, therefore, what the essential function of an out-patients' department should be; they agreed that it must be regarded primarily as a consultant centre for the treatment of cases which could not be treated elsewhere. Edith Mudd, coming from a doctor's family, thought that the hospital should take all cases, whatever their financial status, which would supply the material needed for the education of the students; Anne Cummins, coming straight from her C.O.S. training, thought it important to stress the disgrace of accepting Poor Law Relief unless old age made it absolutely unavoidable. They all deprecated the system of 'letters', issued by the Hospital Saturday Fund to subscribers, which were supposed to give those presenting them a right to be treated at the hospital; and all agreed that they must resist being made into registrars or distributors of relief. They discussed other subjects too, including the importance of the educative work to which the Board of St. George's had taken exception. Edith Mudd produced a carefully drawn up and very simple card of instructions on the feeding and management of infants, which they agreed to sell for a penny to mothers judged sufficiently intelligent to understand the printed word.

The recruitment for the profession increasingly occupied the attention of the committee. The demand for almoners was growing, not very fast, but noticeably. It was of extreme importance to the profession that the right women should be chosen. The parent body, the Administrative Council of the Charity Organization Society, regarded itself as the ultimate authority. The almoners, on the other hand, were unwilling to believe that a committee composed almost entirely of men who had no experience of the day to day work in an almoner's office, could be as capable of choosing the right woman as their own committee. The controversy started in 1904, when the almoners asked the C.O.S. to send to their Committee the names of all the applicants for the post of Almoner, contending that while the original selection of candidates for the social training should be in the hands of the C.O.S., when these had once reached the standard recognized by the Society for their District Secretaries, their suitability as Almoners should be determined by the Almoners' Committee. The C.O.S. was not prepared to accept this view, and for three years the debate continued with varying degrees of acerbity. It was the age-long struggle between the parent and the adolescent offspring; painful, but necessary. The almoners were fully conscious of the debt they owed to Charles Loch, they venerated him and trusted his wisdom, but they were conscious of their own power to govern themselves. They were willing to take advice, but they were not prepared to accept dictation from a body not representing the profession. The position of the Almoners was considerably strengthened by the appointment of a thoroughly unsuitable almoner to Charing Cross Hospital; the appointment had been made by the Central Committee of the C.O.S. without reference to the Almoners' Committee. After this, in 1907, on Loch's suggestion, a joint Council of the C.O.S. and the Almoners was formed and though at first there was some difficulty in agreeing about the proportion of almoners to the non-professional members, a temporarily workable solution was arrived at.

This controversy was the first stage in a protracted struggle by the profession for complete self-government.

4. *Anne Cummins, the first lady almoner at St. Thomas's Hospital*

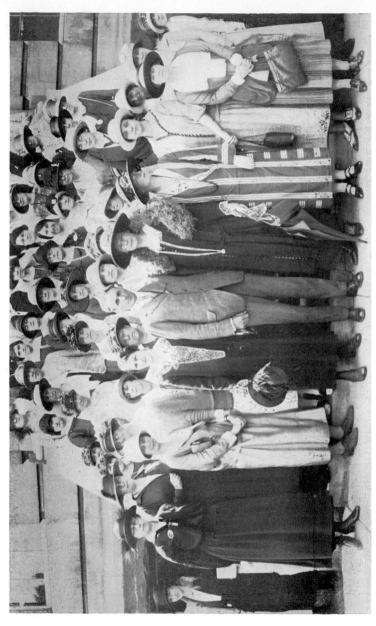

5. Delegates attending the Convention on Social Science, held in Toronto in June 1924. Anne Cummins is in the centre of the picture holding an umbrella.

CHAPTER IV

Enter Anne Cummins

<del>◆━━━◆</del>

'Success depends not on what she knows, but on what she is.'
OCTAVIA HILL on Training of Social Workers

In 1905, St. Thomas's Hospital, at the instigation of the surgeon, Mr. Clutton, whose sister was an eminent member of the Central Committee of the Charity Organization Society, determined to appoint a Lady Almoner. Anne Cummins, recommended by C. S. Loch, was duly appointed. It was an appointment of great moment not only for the Hospital but for the whole future of medical social service, for it was Miss Cummins's vision and her power of realizing it that made of the work of an almoner, hitherto tentative and experimental, a profession universally recognized as an adjunct to the art of healing and an indispensable social service.

It is worthwhile to look at the family whence Anne derived the gifts she was to use so magnificently in the service of her fellows. She was the daughter of the Reverend Henry Cummins and his wife Marieannie, *née* Barnard, whose mother had been a Lyon, a member of the ancient Scottish family. The Barnards belonged to the Sandemanian sect, a dissident group which had broken away from the Scottish Calvinists. It was a stern ultra-Puritan faith; its members accepted the exact literal truth of every word of the Bible, they wished for no beauty but the beauty of holiness in their worship; what singing there was was unaccompanied, led by an elder with a tuning fork; there were no flowers, no adornment of any kind, no appeal to the emotions. While deeply convinced of the supreme importance of religion, all talk of it was discouraged. On the face of it, it seems curious that a girl so brought up, an aristocratic Scot to the tips of her beautiful fingers, emotionally repressed, should have fallen in love with an Irishman from Cork, of great charm, of no particular family, and an ordained priest of the Church of England. But so it was, and no difference about religion ever marred their marital felicity. The children were all brought up as Anglicans and they all adored their beautiful, rather unapproachable mother. Henry Cummins held the living of St. Albans in Wood Street in the East End of London, but when the parish became so overcrowded with warehouses as to make living there impracticable, the Bishop sanctioned his moving to Sion College.

Henry Cummins died early in the 80's, leaving his widow with very little money and seven children, of whom Anne was the fourth. The family moved to Kensington and Anne and her two younger sisters were all sent to Kensington High School. It was a dreary little house in which they were established and there was no money to spare for amenities; of necessity they lived a very frugal life and the children's friends, who visited them, found it an austere household. Idle chatter did not long survive in Mrs. Cummins's presence and her silence

and remoteness were rather alarming to the young. Her
own children, however, were happy enough, and the
family tie held them together in mutual care and affection
long after they had ceased to live together. So that Anne,
in later years, when her professional work was extremely
heavy, yet found time, energy and money to help, not
only Nita, her youngest sister always closest to her in
love and understanding, but also the eldest, Lucia, who
had never been very sympathetic and had indeed been inclined to tyrannize over her juniors. Adolescence is a
difficult time for anyone and for Anne the years were particularly so. She had a warm affection and deep reverence
for her father and she missed him sorely. To begin with
she had found some comfort in the practice of religion,
but when the problems common to adolescents arose in
her mind she grew confused and unhappy and finding no
answer dismissed them as insoluble. She was in many
respects like her mother. She had her mother's air of distinction, her finely chiselled features and her beautiful
hands, but in temperament she was Irish rather than
Scottish; she inherited from her father that Irish charm,
which so wonderfully simplifies the path of those fortunate enough to possess it. It is impossible, even if it were
profitable, to determine from which part of one's ancestry
various traits are derived, but from some part of hers
Anne had inherited a quick intuitive and sympathetic
interest in other people. This is probably the most
valuable gift a social worker can possess, for in contact
with other people to be really interested, to wish to listen
and understand, is the first step towards establishing a
genuine relationship. When to this is added a sense of
humour which eliminates all danger of sentimentality and

keeps the touch light, there is material for the perfect social worker.

When the time came for Anne to leave school, she was naturally anxious to become self-supporting and so relieve the burden on her mother. Her next sister Nellie was considered at school to be unusually gifted mathematically, so it seemed right that she should go to the University. Anne had a very poor opinion of her own intellectual gifts and was all her life apt to overestimate the ability revealed by the possession of a degree; she was sure that Nellie ought to go to the University and that she herself should not. She found a post as governess to two small children, whose parents were taking them to Switzerland. It was a wonderful opportunity for Anne. Switzerland suited her exactly; she had a hunger for beauty, which had been starved in her home; she was never very strong and the confined life, the continual pressure of near poverty, had told on her. Now, in Switzerland, she was free of repressions and the beauty of the mountains was a refreshment to her spirit. Her employers were kind and considerate, they were in every way generous and she enjoyed a normal, healthy life, free from anxieties. But this sort of life could not long be enough for a person of Anne's ability and power. She came back to London, uncertain as to the course she should pursue. She tried teaching, taking a temporary post at the Baker Street Church of England High School (now the Francis Holland School) where her sister Nellie was mathematics mistress. But she found her vocation did not lie in teaching, and as it was obvious that her temperament would lead her to seek work with people rather than with things, she began thinking about social work.

C. S. Loch had been a friend of Henry Cummins. He had kept in touch with the family after his death and he saw in Anne exactly the young woman he wanted to further his schemes for social work; he suggested that she should take the Charity Organization Society's training. Anne agreed readily enough. It was not long before she discovered an appeal in the medical part of the work and the C.O.S. thereupon sent her to work at St. George's Hospital under Edith Mudd. At the end of this training in 1905, when Anne Cummins was thirty-five, she was appointed to St. Thomas's Hospital. She had seen the difficulties at St. George's; she had enough perception to realize that it was no small matter for a hospital with a well-established tradition of service to the community, directed entirely by men of unquestioned authority, to be asked to accept as colleagues professional women not immediately under their control. Miss Cummins accepted this situation; she did not fret at the assumption of male infallibility. She was essentially humble-minded and saw no reason why these distinguished medical men should welcome her assistance until she had proved its value. Her policy, therefore, was to be as inconspicuous as possible. This was not altogether easy, for she was tall and striking in appearance and the fashion of the day—long skirts, sweeping the ground—made moving quickly and quietly difficult. In the early days she always wore her hat in the hospital, hoping that this might suggest to any of the staff whom she met that she was a visitor with no official position, claiming no rights or special consideration. In order to make these encounters rare, she adopted the practice of going outside the Hospital and walking along the street when she had occasion to go from one block to another. The time came, of course, when she could abandon these artifices. At an early stage she won the devotion of Mr. G. Q. Roberts, the Hospital Secretary, who remained her valuable and vocal supporter until they both retired. Those who trained under her in the early days say that the precept on which insistence was most forcibly laid was that they must on no account put a foot wrong with the medical staff. Time was to show that the task of placating the doctors was as nothing to that of winning sisters to regard the almoner as an ally rather than an enemy, but even this was successfully achieved. The Matron at St. Thomas's was a formidable figure and the relationship between her and Miss Cummins was sometimes stormy, a conflict between two giants. The Matron was theoretically very friendly and in many ways a great support, but it was difficult and often intolerable for her to see another woman so powerful yet independent of her jurisdiction.

Most fortunately the reports of the Almoner to her Committee have been preserved and from them it is possible to gain a very clear impression of the work that was accomplished and the spirit in which it was carried out. The reports are good reading. They contain statistics, of course, but these are consigned to an appendix and the body contains an interesting and often amusing account of the problems which have arisen and the way in which they have been tackled. For the writer, believing that she is laying the foundation of a service destined to be of great value to the hospital and to every patient seeking its help, is obviously determined to carry her Committee with her; she is writing to friends, about human beings in whom they must be interested. She had been appointed certainly to check abuse of the out-patients' department and every now and then she throws in a case of fraud which has been detected, but it is perfectly clear that this is not what she considers interesting or even very important, compared to the constructive and positive work on which she is engaged.

It is difficult for us to realize today the conditions which faced Anne Cummins in her work. 'The Poor' no longer exist among us, but at the beginning of the century the great majority of wage earners lived on the border line of poverty and, since no provision was made for sickness or unemployment, when either came, a man's family was plunged into real want. Housing conditions were deplorable; dwellings were overcrowded, bug-ridden and insanitary. Disease was prevalent and tuberculosis flourished. As the 'decline' was accepted as a very natural affliction of the well-to-do a century earlier, so now 'the consumption' was regarded, like unseasonable weather, as just one of those unpleasant manifestations of an incalculable Providence.

Miss Cummins knew what had to be done; she had seen the work at St. George's, and what had been begun there must be carried on from St. Thomas's; it was a matter of education. The laws of hygiene, the importance of fresh air and nourishing food must somehow be inculcated. She was fortunate in finding much good pioneer work being done in Lambeth by rather unusual people in the attempt to tackle the problems. The clergy of Lambeth, men such as the Rev. Thory Gage-Gardner (later one of the Canons of Canterbury), the Rev. F. O. T. Hawkes (later Bishop of Kingston) were very socially minded. The Lady Margaret Hall Settlement was a real centre of social work and the Charity Organization Society was extremely active. All these people were encouraged by having a newly started centre of social work in the Hospital backed by an excellent Samaritan Fund. There was a great deal of co-operation and of planning together on general social problems. The foundations of the work for the tuberculous were laid on sound lines; Anne Cummins got some windows opened, some wives taught how to procure and cook the most nourishing meals for a sick man; she managed to get shelters, like the Morrison shelters of our own war days, to provide out of door sleeping accommodation, and she badgered landlords into putting their houses into a reasonable state of repair for the tubercular tenant. It was little enough that she could do, but the foundations were so soundly laid that when she obtained command of more money and therefore more workers it was possible on those foundations to build a service developed, but never superseded, even when it was taken over by the State.

Nowadays, problems of maternity and child welfare constitute a large part of our social service. It was not so at the beginning of the century. Though all doctors and those concerned in social work were indeed troubled at the rate of infant mortality, which remained obstinately high, the general public was unaware of the facts, and the Government so little awake to their importance that, when the First International Conference on Infant Mortality was held in Paris in 1905, Great Britain was not one of the twenty-eight countries represented, though three Local Authorites—Battersea, Huddersfield and Glasgow —sent delegates. In France the problem was taken seriously, for a sharp and long continued fall in the birthrate had aroused apprehension as to the danger of de-population. In 1892 Professor Pierre Budin of the Charité Hospital in Paris had established a scheme of regular consultation, lasting for two years, on all babies born in his hospital. He had also demonstrated the importance of clean milk in the feeding of infants. These lessons were not without their effect in England. As early as 1899 Dr. Drew Harris, Medical Officer of Health, had applied them in St. Helens, where he established centres for distributing sterilized milk and made the distribution the occasion of consultation with the mothers. In 1905 Dr. Eric Pritchard in Marylebone opened consultation centres for maternity cases and these developed into centres for teaching mothercraft. Shortly after this a School for Mothers was established in St. Pancras.

When Anne Cummins began her work in St. Thomas's the campaign for the lives of babies was in its early stages. It was a fight against both ignorance and poverty, but the educational front was the more important. Miss Cummins brought to the task that sensitive sympathy which charac-terized all her dealings with other people, and all her in-telligent powers of organization. Lambeth was like other working-class districts. In houses with no water except what was fetched in a bucket from a tap down the street it is not to be wondered at that there was no standard of cleanliness and, since at that time there was no maternity ward in any general hospital, children were born at home in very unpromising conditions. For the most part ex-pectant mothers accepted the situation stoically; they made no preparation for the new arrival, prepared neither clothes nor cot; made no plan for the actual event and, as often as not, it was not until the labour began that the husband or a neighbour appeared at the hospital asking for help.

In tackling this situation Miss Cummins was not only up to date, but well ahead of her contemporaries, for it was not until 1913 that any other hospital—Edinburgh Maternity Hospital—organized pre-natal visiting. It was in 1907 that Miss Cummins managed to persuade her reluctant hospital authority to accept this startling innovation, in face of its anxiety lest home visits and insistence on the elements of hygiene might alienate the district and so deprive students of cases. She got her way and the hospital announced it would deal with no mother who had not registered the coming birth in good time. Thus there was regular pre-natal visiting, whose objects were two-fold: to improve the material conditions and to educate the expectant family. The first of these tasks involved tackling the landlord and the sanitary authority and persisting until the necessary improvements had been made; the second was a more difficult thing involving patience and tact in steady regular educative work. The mother must be helped to make clothes for her coming baby, she must be taught to believe in and to practise habits of cleanliness. Maternity clubs were started where mothers could meet and enjoy the comfort of a cup of tea to lighten the business of education. The visits of course did not cease with the arrival of the baby; there was still much to learn about the care of an infant; about diet, the necessity of fresh air and of acquiring habits of sleep. The work succeeded to a remarkable degree. Many mothers learned to provide better and more nourishing food for themselves and their babies. These were brought to the hospital, where Anne Cummins and Dr. Fairbairn spent many hours weighing them and advising on their treatment. Some mothers were dissuaded from a hurried weaning of the child in order to enable them to go out to work—a practice regarded with great disfavour except in cases of real necessity.

Those concerned in maternity welfare were naturally most anxious about the feeding of nursing mothers. In 1906 a much subsidized meals centre for mothers had been started in Chelsea, where at the cost of 1d. a substantial meal could be obtained. This scheme was adopted in other parts of London, and in 1908, a year of very severe poverty among the working classes, Lambeth proposed to inaugurate it. Miss Cummins's reaction to this proposal is interesting and characteristic. She reports that 'Fortunately this scheme was not adopted. Any movement of this kind would be disastrous to the neighbourhood and would undermine much of the present effort to raise the people from pauperization.'

It is important to understand Anne Cummins's point of view in this matter. She was a convinced believer in the principles of charitable administration inculcated by the C.O.S. The fundamental principle can be stated easily enough; it was that every man is responsible for the nurture and sustenance of his own family, that if through sickness or other misfortune he is unable to fulfil this obligation, he must be helped by the charity of others and this must be administered always with the end in view of making him able to resume his own responsibility as soon as possible. Those who were unwilling or perhaps unable to make the necessary effort to stand on their own feet Miss Cummins classed, not as the undeserving but as the unhelpable, and to begin giving money to these was simply pouring it away. Since this money came from the pockets of other people, it was obviously important to use it constructively. Nor was she concerned only as a trustee for the money; she belonged to a generation which believed in spiritual, rather than material values. She believed that material assistance could corrupt and that not only the family but the whole of society was damaged by the short-sighted policy of 'feeding mothers and babies gratuitously, in a wholesale manner'. That she found the principle hard to apply cannot be doubted. 'It is heart rending', she wrote, 'to refuse help to a woman in her confinement because her husband is a drunkard or a loafer. But if the husband is able-bodied and can get work, it is clearly inadvisable to step in and remove the impetus that might rouse him to his duty, and if a man spends half his earnings in the public house, it is clearly wrong to support his wife and thus remove the responsibility from his shoulders.'

This doctrine sounds strange to modern ears. For better or for worse the idea that a man has a moral obligation to support himself and his family has gone, and since the Exchequer—believed to be bottomless—will provide the cash, there need be no more heartbreak of this particular sort for the social worker.

But while the indiscriminate feeding of expectant mothers seemed utterly wrong, Anne Cummins believed there was a case for helping those who, through no fault of their own, could not provide for themselves. Having made the most searching inquiry into their circumstances and established, beyond all possibility of doubt that the husband was doing all he could and that the mother was a good and careful manager, she gave free rein to her generous impulses and provided the necessary meals, ordaining that they should be served at 2 p.m. so that every mother should be able to give the rest of the family its dinner and send the children to school. Then the meal was to become a social occasion; the mothers were given their dinner in the private room of an eating house, reserved for them; they were attended by one of the hospital visitors and discussion on the various ways of preparing dishes or on cheap forms of nourishing food was encouraged, and the women had a happy hour in that exchange of confidences and sharing of recipes so dear to the heart of all women whose life consists mainly in running a home. So the maternity work flourished and it was not long before, in this department as in that of the tubercular patients, Miss Cummins's resources were extended.

CHAPTER V

The Northcote Trust

◁─────▷

'What would you do if someone gave you £500—
No—I mean £5,000?'

DR. HOWITT to Anne Cummins

In 1905, the very year in which Anne Cummins was
appointed to St. Thomas's Hospital, a similar experiment was started on the other side of the Atlantic at
the Massachusetts General Hospital, Boston, where at the
instigation of Dr. Richard Cabot, a great physician and a
man of outstanding sympathy and imagination, Miss Ida
Cannon was appointed as a social worker. In 1907, soon
after her appointment, Miss Cannon came to England to
see what was being done in this country and she was
naturally sent to St. Thomas's, where equally naturally
she was at once captivated by Anne Cummins, the charm
of her personality and the value of her work, so closely
allied to her own. A warm friendship ensued which was
kept up by correspondence and lasted to the end of Miss
Cummins's life. Nor did her death break the link. When,
in 1955, both the Almoners' Department of St. Thomas's
Hospital and the Social Service Department of Massachusetts General Hospital were celebrating their Jubilees,

Miss Cummins's successor, Miss Cherry Morris, went from the gathering in London to Boston, where Miss Cannon herself presided over a vast concourse of medical social workers drawn from every part of the United States and from different parts of the world.

In 1909 a wonderful thing happened to Anne Cummins. As she sat in her office, Dr. Howitt came in and asked her: 'What would you do if someone gave you £500?' It was an easy question to answer and she replied without hesitation, 'I should start almoners working in the wards'. Dr. Howitt departed saying no more, but the next day he returned. 'I say,' he said, 'I made a mistake, it was £5,000.' Anne Cummins's mind leapt at once to the possibilities opening before her. It had come about in this way. In 1908 Stafford Northcote was a patient in St. Thomas's Home where he was attended by Dr. A. B. Howitt, who from the beginning had been one of Anne Cummins's staunchest supporters. Stafford Northcote was suffering from a serious illness and when he was sufficiently recovered to leave the Home, it was thought that a tour abroad would be beneficial and he begged Dr. Howitt to accompany him. The tour took them to Boston and there Dr. Howitt visited Dr. Cabot, who introduced them to Miss Cannon and showed them the social work which he had instituted. Stafford Northcote was immensely interested and impressed by this en-lightened innovation and was astonished to be told by Miss Cannon and Dr. Howitt that this work was no different from that which had been going on for four years at St. Thomas's. Dr. Howitt managed to enlighten him on the subject and when Stafford Northcote asked his advice about the form to be taken for a memorial to his sister Cicely, who had died at the age of nineteen, was able to persuade him that the endowment of this kind of work at St. Thomas's would be an admirable plan.

This led to the foundation of the Cicely Northcote Trust. Its constitution was drawn up by Mr. Northcote and Dr. Howitt in close consultation with Anne Cummins. The conception was a bold one; the Trust was not to be merely another fund for the relief of the sick, it was to be an instrument of research, which should benefit a far larger section of the community than the patients at St. Thomas's. It should work with charitable societies, with clergy and welfare workers to relieve suffering, but its primary function was to study the social causes of ill health and to endeavour to tackle them. It was to appoint almoners, fully trained and adequately paid to attempt whatever work at the moment seemed the most promising and to share the results of any successful experiment with any organization that could make use of it. Trustees were appointed; not for the most part from those with honoured names that demand respect, but from young people who were already interested in social work and were eager to make experiments. One of these, Mr. Howarth, is its Chairman at the present day.

The Rules for the administration of the Trust were drawn up with the utmost care. They were designed to give as much freedom as possible to the Executive Officer, so that they might make a supple instrument in her hand. The wisdom and forethought shown in this Constitution is evidenced by the fact that after fifty years it is not outdated, but forms a satisfactory framework for the projects of today.

To the Hospital and the public the Northcote Trust

Almoners were exactly on the same terms as the other Almoners, but Anne Cummins had gained freedom and quicker powers of extension. Hitherto the Almoner's Department had been financed entirely by the Hospital and since then, as now, there was never quite enough money to do all that needed doing, Miss Cummins had been obliged to restrict her demands to the essential, to refrain from asking for more staff and therefore herself to do much detailed work that could equally well have been delegated to a less fully trained worker. The Northcote Trust did not give her enough money to carry out all the schemes that surged in her mind—what pioneer outside the Arabian Nights could ever imagine such wealth?—but it did give her an income on which she could draw without encroaching on the general hospital funds.

The terms of the Trust provided that work should be undertaken in three directions; in the wards, for tuberculous patients and for maternity cases. Northcote workers were at once appointed for these purposes. Work was begun in two wards and by the end of the first year had been extended to seven. This work was not essentially different from what had been done for the out-patients ever since Anne Cummins's appointment. It was somewhat easier perhaps, for the worker could call upon each patient, and in the comparative quiet of the ward, make friends with each. The patient, withdrawn for the moment from family distractions, and perhaps bored by the long intervals between visiting hours, was ready enough to talk to someone who appeared to have the time and the inclination to listen. From these friendly informal chats, the worker was able to gain a pretty accurate idea of the patient's economic position and the resources,

E   65

mental and material, he possessed wherewith to return to a normal life. One respect in which the ward work differed from the out-patients' was in the presence in the wards of many sick who had come in from the country and who were therefore outside the scope of the local charities. In these cases reference was made to the clergy of the parish from which the sick came, to local landowners and to employers. A very satisfactory liaison was thus established between the hospital and the clergy and charitable organizations over a wide area.

The work done for tubercular patients was simply an extension of that begun by Anne Cummins before the foundation of the Northcote Trust. Having more money and therefore more workers, she was able to cover more ground. Now all tubercular patients were referred to the Almoners. They were classified by the physicians and those in the early stages of the disease were given sanatorium treatment at the expense of the Northcote Trust. The records show that about 20 per cent of the patients fell into this category and of these 80 per cent were sufficiently cured to return to normal healthy occupations, though they still needed supervision and help. At the other end of the scale 15 per cent were either in a very advanced stage of the disease or quite destitute and these were handed over to the Guardians, who alone administered institutions in which such cases could be cared for and prevented from becoming a danger to the public. The 65 per cent remaining lived in their own homes and needed to be taught how to do so properly. The method for dealing with this 65 per cent is described by Miss Cummins in her report, made to the National Association for the Prevention of Tuberculosis, in 1910.

Nowadays we all know so well the things that are prescribed for tubercular patients—nourishing food, rest, fresh air and sanitary living conditions—that it seems hardly worth mentioning them. At the beginning of the century they were not so well known, and Anne Cummins had immense difficulty and took immense pains to educate these patients in their own homes. 'Special care', she says, 'is taken not to be didactic. It is harder to educate than to instruct, but unless the patient is educated no lasting good can be effected. At first all seems quite impossible and, as is only natural, many of them are stolidly hopeless and do not evince the slightest interest in their condition. But when gradually they realize that we mean business and intend really to improve matters; when their hopelessness is met by an equally stolid determination to help them, they themselves begin to wake up.' To persuade the patients to eat the right food was difficult, not only because they had no idea of anything more nourishing than substitute meat drinks, but because the price of milk was prohibitive, inevitably so in an age without refrigeration or speed of transport; and, as Anne Cummins says, 'Lentils, haricot beans, oatmeal are almost unknown, and are regarded with suspicion'.

All this educative work, and the improvement of the material conditions in which these people lived, was tackled by visitors drawn from all the local voluntary societies. 'We should achieve very little', says Miss Cummins, 'were it not for the co-operation of outside agencies. We do not hesitate to call upon anyone to assist and rarely meet with a refusal, for this is a form of personal service which appeals to most. The neighbour next door, the priest and the employer are generally willing to join hands, and in enlisting their help we feel that the work is extending beyond the actual case in question.'

One part of this report reveals most clearly the chasm which separates us from those days. 'Unless the physician specially orders it, no one is advised to leave off work, we only try to improve the patient's capacity for work. It will be most dangerous to remove from work cases which are not up to the standard required for sanatorium treatment, nor so advanced as to be suitable for incurables' homes or for the infirmary . . . for work means food, and starvation is worse than consumption.'

This reveals a society which has entirely passed away. The poverty which made the provision of adequate food for a sick man a matter of serious difficulty no longer exists among us; and we may be thankful that the reflection 'starvation is worse than consumption' has no relevance to day. The knowledge and, to some extent, the practice of sound hygiene is no longer rare. There is a much higher level of education and much of the educative work undertaken by the almoners and visitors in the homes of the tubercular would today be superfluous. There are still overcrowded and insanitary houses in our cities, but they are fortunately not as general as these workers found them to be. Medical science has reduced tuberculosis in this country to manageable dimensions. For the improved conditions we cannot fail to be thankful. But there is no gain without loss. In these early days each case sent to a sanatorium was a real personal adventure. For a long time a box of primroses came each year to Miss Cummins from the first patient for whom she had been able to arrange sanatorium treatment and who remained grateful all his life.

There is something friendly and heart-warming in Anne Cummins's account of the cordial co-operation of neighbours, clergy, officials and social workers to help those who needed help, and perhaps the substitution of officials and regulations for voluntary workers and improvised methods is not pure gain.

This work for the tuberculous done at St. Thomas's has been described in some detail because the records there are fully kept and available, but of course the understanding of the disease and its social implications had spread and the same kind of work was being done in connection with many hospitals. In Brompton Hospital, more particularly, because it specialized in chest diseases, the scope of the work was immense and was most ably organized by Miss Marx, who had worked under Miss Mudd in Leeds. The reputation of her work was international and visitors from far and wide came to study it and learn how to adapt it to their own conditions.

In maternity, as in tuberculosis cases, the Northcote Trust made it possible to extend the work which Anne Cummins had so ably begun. There were more workers, there was a little more money to spend. It could profitably be spent on expectant mothers who were ordered 'rest'—an order which seemed fantastic to a mother with a house to run, a husband to feed and other children to care for. The almoner, with a little money to spend, could often find a respectable neighbour, willing to act as home help for a small wage, and she could then persuade the mother that what the doctor ordered was really possible and necessary.

An almoner attended every session of the gynaecological department and subsequently visited all maternity cases, doing in each home the work which hospital visitors had been doing under Miss Cummins's direction ever since she had been appointed; there was the same careful scrutiny of all the conditions, the same anxiety to ensure that no help which could demoralize the recipient should be given; again we find the mothers being exhorted to save for the arrival of the newcomer and in one report the fact that a father has added from his 'pocket money' a subscription to the 'new baby fund' is recorded with pleasure, not primarily on account of the material addition, but because it is a recognition on the part of the father that the coming event is of moment to him as well as to his wife.

But the Northcote Trust also made an important innovation in the maternity work in St. Thomas's Hospital. Hitherto there had been no maternity ward in any general hospital; there were lying-in hospitals—but not many—and there were lying-in wards in the infirmaries, but these were run by the Guardians and the taint of the Poor Law was upon them. The proposition was now made that St. Thomas's should institute a maternity ward. The project was carefully considered with great anxiety, so common at that date, as to whether it might not demoralize those who ought to be able to make provision for the birth of their children at home, paying a midwife or general practitioner. After much discussion it was determined that a maternity ward should be opened, but admission to it should be very carefully restricted. Eligible cases were to be those who on account of poor general health or of some complication in their physical condition were likely to need special medical attention; or those whose husbands had done their utmost to make provision for the birth, but owing to misfortune such as unemployment or accident had failed to provide what was necessary. These cases seemed obviously suitable, but there were two more classes rather unexpected at that date. The first were those rather 'above the level of the working classes'; expectant mothers whose husbands could not afford a nursing home, who lived in small houses in conditions which made privacy impossible. It was felt that these were more sensitive than the ordinary working-class women and suffered more from lack of privacy, from the general discomfort and confusion in the household while they were laid up. Their husbands could pay something and were eager to do so. These cases were to be admitted and since the hospitals were free and could make no charge, the husband was invited to make a voluntary contribution. The last category to be admitted was the unmarried mother. Here it was necessary to tread very delicately. To admit the unmarried freely would have destroyed the value of the ward, for no respectable woman would have applied for admission. Anne Cummins had a great tenderness for the young; it was the young girl who had 'got into trouble' as the phrase ran, who in a less sophisticated generation was terrified and alone, probably afraid to tell her parents and seeing no possible future for herself or the child she was so calamitously to bring into a hostile world; it was these girls whom Miss Cummins longed to help and the establishment of the 'Mary Ward' made it possible to give this help. In the ward the girl found kindness instead of hostility, she was helped to face the future, to make a plan for herself and for the infant; and many started life afresh with new hope and courage.

The work of the Northcote Trust expanded rapidly. In

October 1912, in its Third Annual Report, the Trust made an appeal for more and increased subscriptions, not to increase but to maintain its activities. By this time work was undertaken in every ward and this involved the appointment of more staff and the provision of a new and more spacious office, which had already become a useful meeting place for all local social workers, from outside the hospital as well as those working in it. In March of the same year, Miss Cummins had made a report on the work of the almoners in the out-patient department. She reviewed the result of the seven years since her appointment. The achievement of the department was not inconsiderable; cases of fraud were practically unknown; poor law cases and chronic sick no longer thronged the out-patient department; no case recommended by the staff was ignored; tubercular and maternity cases were regularly visited and supervised. There was a welcome increase of co-operation with Local Authorities, notably with the London County Council.

All this work, whether done by almoners paid by the Hospital or by the Northcote Trust, was under Miss Cummins's direction and this, of necessity, to some extent altered the character of her own work. It was no longer her duty to interview each applicant, unravelling the perplexities of a mind little used to explaining itself coherently. She was now the Director of a big organization and her task was rather to direct its policy, appoint its officers, interpret its work to those whom it would serve and to other organizations which should work with it, but she did not lose touch with the patients. She went round to each department every day and almoners kept all their difficulties on which to consult her. A fellow worker remembers an occasion when an applicant was brought to the office in a state of mulish non-co-operation; she had perhaps been not too tactfully handled by an in-experienced almoner; hostility bristled from every pore; the worker who introduced her was hot and bothered. The Lady Almoner was writing at her desk; she put down her pen, put one elbow on the desk resting her chin on her hand and with a characteristic motion of the other hand, suggesting that she had all the time in the world to spare, said in a gentle confiding way, 'Now, what's all this trouble about?' The effect was instantaneous; the woman, who had come in prepared to assert and if neces-sary fight for her rights, was utterly disarmed, burst into tears and in an incredibly short time was discussing her problems in a spirit of completely friendly co-operation. In moments of crisis, too, Miss Cummins was at once in demand. She describes an occasion when she received an S.O.S. from the mental ward and hurrying thither, found an anxious doctor confronting a woman surrounded by shoes in every state of decrepitude scattered all over the floor. As Miss Cummins came in the woman was declaim-ing, 'Tell me where to find four shillings to mend each of those shoes, and then you can cure me'. Miss Cummins accepted the challenge; the woman and the shoes were taken away, the husband was visited and it was found that he could, and when asked would, mend the shoes himself.

Increasingly the doctors found themselves depending on Miss Cummins's wisdom and the students acquired the habit of slipping into the Almoner's office to ask advice about the gloves and ties they were about to buy, as well as about the more serious matters.

Appointing staff was a heavy part of Miss Cummins's work. The demand for almoners was now exceeding the supply and it was often her task to assess the quality of a young woman wishing to undertake the work. She had a quick eye for the likely candidate and her judgement, though not always conventional, was generally sound. Mrs. Ramsay, for many years her secretary, relates that 'L.A.', as she was commonly designated by those who worked with her, came into the office where she was working as a typist and said, 'I want you to come and work in my room'. Mrs. Ramsay was taken aback; she had taken a secretarial course rather late in her life, when she was widowed, and she was very conscious that she was less experienced and less highly trained than many of the younger girls in her office. She protested therefore, 'But I'm not nearly quick or smart enough.' 'All the same, I want you,' said L.A. and so it was, and Mrs. Ramsay served her in complete harmony for many years and continued under her successor, Miss Morris, to be the support and stay of the Almoners' Department, only leaving in 1946. Another worker tells that when she was training for welfare work she was suddenly sent by the Principal of her Training College to be interviewed by the Lady Almoner. She had not made up her mind about her future and she felt she must be making a very poor impression, so she was astonished when she heard L.A. say, 'Then you'll begin on Monday'. She replied, 'But I don't know yet if I've passed my exam.' To which L.A. replied calmly, 'Well, if you haven't you'll take it again,' and the interview was at an end.

Anne Cummins was working harder than she had ever done, and some of her friends, watching her, feared lest she was driving herself beyond her physical capacity. They carried her off for holidays abroad and were astonished at her vigour and resilience. After these holidays she returned to the hospital full of the energy which is given to those who are doing work in which they believe whole-heartedly and with and for those who trust them. This good fortune was hers. The hospital authorities were beginning to trust her, her colleagues enjoyed her; her clients depended on her and she knew she was serving them.

CHAPTER VI

The Insurance Act and Work in the Provinces

◆━━━━◆

> '*It is in the best interests of the majority of patients that the fullest use shall in future be made of legislative and charitable efforts combined.*'
>
> ANNE CUMMINS, 1913

M iss Cummins's annual reports contained more than an account of the work accomplished by her department during the year. In them she reviewed the state of the society with which she was dealing and her comments thereon throw an interesting light on current social changes as they appeared to contemporary eyes. 1911 was a difficult year; an exceptionally hot summer brought with it a severe epidemic of dysentery; the distress among the poor of Lambeth and South London generally was acute and Miss Cummins was moved to pity for the sufferers and indignation at the indifference of the general public. 'For weeks', she writes, 'the casualty was crowded with babies. . . . The position was so acute that, as the municipal authorites took no steps, the hospital authorities felt obliged to relax their strict regulations . . . preserved milk was granted to all who seemed unable to provide it. . . . Only those who watched the patients daily could realize the suffering and misery and those who had to deal with them could not but feel that if the epidemic had attacked grown-up people instead of speechless babies the public would have been moved to special efforts of relief.'

The summer with its epidemic passed, but the autumn brought new difficulties. There was much industrial unrest and strikes broke out which greatly impoverished the hospital clientele. Anne Cummins realized that many of the strikers, especially the women, were inadequately paid, but, believing as she did that industrial disputes must be 'fought out between employers and employed', she found it very difficult to determine the right course to pursue in the matter of giving relief to the families of strikers. The strikes left behind them a legacy of much bitterness and general dissatisfaction 'which', says she, 'may be quite healthy among honest workers, but which is wholly unsatisfactory when voiced by the idle and unemployable'. The first Insurance Act followed. 'The necessity of voluntary provision against sickness and times out of work has been upheld for many years by the hospital.' Indeed from the beginning the almoners one and all had unwearyingly—and for the most part fruitlessly—exhorted all their clients to subscribe to provident dispensaries in days of prosperity in order to insure against days of misfortune. They had urged thrift ceaselessly, on the grounds of self-respect. Now a contribution was to be demanded by the law. Not to be obliged to appeal to the better nature of those who did not care to respond was no doubt a relief, but Miss Cummins found it hard to accept it. 'The necessity of an Act of Parliament to enforce such a provision may be questioned,' she wrote, but whether necessary or not, the thing was done and she was concerned to work within it rather than to discuss it, to study it rather than to criticize it. For the Act was of immense importance. She says of it, 'Probably no measure that has ever been passed has had so deep-seated and far-reaching an effect on medical charities.' The first important step to take was to see that everyone connected with the Almoner's department should thoroughly understand the Act. To this end Miss Cummins arranged a course of lectures on the subject and, since the Act as originally presented had several defects, which were dealt with by amendments, the serious study of it continued for a considerable period.

The Act brought new categories into the world of the hospital—the insured and the uninsured—and this raised certain difficulties. At St. Thomas's, ever since Miss Cummins had been appointed, a system of registration of patients had been in force and the only development needed in the system was its extension to Casualty. When this was done, all the information required for the purposes of the Act was available. There remained, however, certain suspicions, harboured by subscribers and expressed by the Hospital Saturday Fund and by certain of the provident societies. These bodies were inclined to feel that the medical care given by the Hospital was better than that given by the panel doctors and they held the view that those who had subscribed to the Hospital Saturday Fund or to a Friendly Society had an absolute right to treatment by the hospital. Constant complaints therefore were received that this or that subscriber had been refused treatment on the grounds that he was an insured person. The allegations were invariably untrue, but each had to be investigated and the practice of the Hospital explained. In fact the practice of the Hospital had not changed; each patient was examined by the medical staff, irrespective of his status as insured or uninsured. He was treated in Hospital if his medical condition warranted it, and otherwise referred to his panel or his private doctor as the case might be.

There were some subscribers to the Northcote Trust who supposed, when the Act was passed, there would be no need for them to subscribe to the Trust, since the State would supply the money needed. Miss Cummins explained that this was far from being the case, 'though it is possible', she writes, 'that the number of temporary allowances required will be decreased; that the grants for phthisic patients may be smaller, it is doubtful whether this will diminish the expenditure to any appreciable extent.' There were many patients in the uninsured category, but apart from that, there was no provision for the dependant even of an insured man, except for maternity. Moreover, the State inevitably gives benefits on a uniform basis; it is a matter of filling in a form and getting whatever is agreed to as fair for an average case, but in fact no man is the average, each one is a special case, the needs are infinitely varied and no general assessment can be fair to all. It is on this that Anne Cummins insists again and again in all her reports and in all her thinking about her cases. Each is an individual and is treated as such; slow careful work, patient thought, quick sensitive sympathy must be brought to bear on every problem in order that the right help may be given at the right time. For the problems are very rarely purely material. They are far more often emotional and psychological and these things cannot be adjusted by the simple handing over of a sum of money, however considerable.

The report to the subscribers to the Northcote Trust in October 1913 was written, not by Miss Cummins, but by senior members of the hospital staff. The suggestion came from them and was joyfully accepted by the Almoner, who saw in it the reward of all her years of patient wooing of the staff. So completely had she conquered initial prejudices that the staff was now eager to testify to the subscribers to the value of the almoners' work in the hospital. Sections of the report were therefore contributed by senior members of the staff, the physician, the surgeon, the obstetrician and the tuberculosis superintendent. All paid tribute to the almoners. Subscribers could not doubt the official approval of the way in which the money they subscribed was being spent. Yet possibly, as they read the laudatory reports of the work done, they wondered why they were so much less easy to read than the annual reports to which they were accustomed. For to a modern reader there is no doubt that the reports of these eminent men of science are dull; they use a great many words to state rather obvious truths; they cite cases to illustrate a thesis but no one comes to life, as all Anne Cummins's cases do. They speak of 'a mother anxious for the welfare of her little ones', where she speaks of the mother 'fretting lest the children are being sent to school unwashed—or worse—uncombed'. For Anne Cummins's reports were about real individuals whom she knew and cared about, there is vitality in every line she writes and a glint of laughter at their absurdities. She tells of a young man whose tale of misfortune was 'so confused and improbable that it must have been true'; of the impoverished Frenchwoman hoping only that death might take her before her savings were exhausted, who after long and careful handling melted into unreserve and 'revealed the glorious fact that Edward VII had once spoken to her and had remembered her name'. There is a zest in all Miss Cummins's writings which makes them easy reading and we may well believe that the subscribers, gratified as they were by official commendation of the work to which they subscribed, nevertheless turned back with relief to the animated reports they were wont to receive.

Miss Cummins had written a postscript to the report of 1913. 'It must be remembered that the work of a Social Service Department on the scale of that adopted at St. Thomas's Hospital should be judged largely as a pioneer effort. There is no precedent for much of the work and step by step each new development has to be planned. There are weak spots to be found and many failures could be shown, which are only too apparent to those immediately responsible for them. The linking up and strengthening of the various branches into one co-ordinating whole is the work now to be faced. Modern legislation is extending rapidly to all questions of social reform. Side by side with internal alterations, constant readjustments are needed with Municipal and Poor Law authorities and such readjustment is necessarily often of a delicate and difficult nature. But it is in the best interests of the majority of the patients for whom the hospital exists, that the fullest use shall in future be made of legislative and charitable efforts combined.'

To this task Miss Cummins now set herself. To one brought up in the Victorian tradition, it was not easy.

Instinctively, she distrusted regulation, compulsion even for a good end—and any sort of regimentation. It is a measure of her intelligence and her adaptability—which is humility—that she forthwith accepted a scheme so foreign to her nature and worked it with the utmost good will. First there were relations to be established with the panel doctors. The Governors of the Hospital ordained that insured persons should not be treated by the Hospital unless referred by the panel doctor as requiring treatment he was unable to give. This was, in some cases, not in the best interests of the patient, for the panel doctor inevitably saw and treated him as an isolated individual, whereas the Hospital, looking at him in the context of his social setting, was often able to give not only medical but social relief. The Almoner cites the case of a girl sent for surgical boots for flat feet. 'She was found to be doing unsuitable and heavy work, and was afraid to change it, as she and her widowed mother were keeping themselves and a younger sister still at school on their joint earnings. The girl was sent for convalescence and provided with surgical boots; on her return she was apprenticed to a skilled trade and is now doing well. Her earnings were supplemented for some time to enable her mother to forego the extra money of her previous employment. The mother was found to be suffering in health because of her great need of teeth. She was provided with a set of teeth, and her health has so far improved that she is now able to earn steadily at her own trade. The family are still constantly visited by members of the Skilled Employment Association, who co-operated in the case with the Hospital, the Society for the Relief of Distress and the C.O.S. The initial request was for surgical boots. It resulted in:

convalescence, surgical boots, apprenticeship to a skilled trade for the patient. Monetary allowance for the family. Artificial teeth, improved health and more regular wages for the mother.' At first the panel doctors found it difficult to recognize which patients could, or could not, be accepted by the Hospital, but gradually an understanding was reached, and there was no longer need for refusing patients mistakenly recommended by the doctor.

There was also the necessity of adjusting relations with municipal authorities, who were becoming increasingly aware of the importance of health to the well-being of the community. School medical inspections were instituted, baby clinics, dental clinics and clinics for the inspection of schoolchildren and children under school age were established and from all these, cases were referred to the hospital. In the early days of school medical inspection, children swarmed into the casualty department referred by school doctors, arriving unaccompanied by parents, and often needing, not medical attention, but cleansing operations. This, however, did not last long. In co-operation with school care committees a reasonable system was established, by which only children in need of hospital treatment were referred.

Altogether, as Miss Cummins surveyed the work done and that which lay before her, she felt a reasonable confidence in the future. Co-operation with other charitable organizations had always been satisfactory. Now Local Authorities, Insurance Committees and other public bodies were increasingly willing to work with the Hospital, which was playing an immensely important part in the life of the district, and its influence was steadily increasing.

The expansion of the work at St. Thomas's was not an

isolated phenomenon. Londoners are apt to believe that they are in advance of the rest of the country, but the facts do not always support this faith. As early as October 1906, while St. George's was fretting about Edith Mudd's intelligent experiments and Anne Cummins was using all her tact and charm to disarm the doctors at St. Thomas's, the medical staff of the Norfolk and Norwich Hospital met and passed a Resolution, apparently without any dissentient, that out-patients should be seen by an almoner and only those admitted who were found suitable after inquiry. The system of admission to the out-patients' department by 'outdoor recommendation'— presumably the 'letters' from subscribers practised elsewhere, was thereby abolished and C. R. Waley started her work as 'Honorary Almoner' in January 1907. The adjective 'Honorary' may have facilitated the smooth running of the work, or it may be that there is more consciousness of fellowship in a county town and a cathedral city than is to be found in the metropolis—so overcrowded that the sense of community is lost. Whatever the cause, Miss Waley appears to have met with no difficulties beyond those inherent in any job dealing with human beings. Co-operation was freely forthcoming and the work flourished. In 1913, when Miss Waley retired, a paid almoner was appointed to carry on the work.

While in London and the Home Counties the number of almoners employed steadily increased, the industrial cities hung back; inquiries came perpetually, from Sheffield, Birmingham, Glasgow. The inquiries were answered, but there the matter rested. Leeds was the first of the great industrial cities to employ an almoner. The appointment was due to Charles Lupton, the Chairman

of the Hospital Board, which controlled not only the
General Infirmary but also the Public Dispensary and the
Women and Children's Hospital. Charles Lupton had
seen something of the work of an almoner at the London
Hospital, whose Chairman was a friend of his; he had
become convinced of the great potentialities for good in
such an appointment and was determined to make one in
Leeds. The Board was not altogether easy to convince;
every member of the Honorary Staff was *ipso facto* a member
of the Board and no appointment could be made without
its consent. The professional members of the Board were
not disposed to give great weight to the opinion of a lay-
man, even though he were their Chairman, and he did not
easily get his way. But the Board as a whole was apathetic
rather than hostile, and finally the appointment was made.
The new almoner was Edith Mudd. She was put in
charge of the three hospitals and an assistant and a student
were appointed to work under her. Edith Mudd, after her
experience at St. George's, was not likely to expect an
easy situation. Some members of the staff were definitely
hostile, the resident medical officer at first refused to
allow her to see any patients and, as in the early days at
the hospitals in London, the medical staff tended to regard any 'outsider' as an intruder and to resent these
women who 'interfered' with their patients. Edith Mudd
refused to be discouraged; she had in Leeds, what she
had never had at St. George's, the unstinted support of
the Chairman of her Governors and she set herself
resolutely and patiently to capture the staff. It was the
younger men who first began to see the point of the work.
A young assistant physician appointed in 1912 was the
first who really understood how greatly the almoner

85

could serve him and his patients. This was the turning point, for once a member of the staff was really converted, faith in the work began to spread.

The work was very hard. At first the almoners were obliged to do their own visiting, since voluntary workers were not forthcoming, but the appointment of a new and very able secretary to the Leeds C.O.S. helped considerably. He was able to organize a 'Children's Committee' on which all local charities and parish organizations were represented and this simplified for the almoners the business of collaborating with outside charitable agencies, always an important part of their work. The tasks of the almoners did not differ greatly from those carried out in London. Poverty, bad housing and insanitary conditions existed in Leeds as in London, and though overcrowding in Leeds was less than in London, there was an acute evil arising from back to back housing and a great prevalence of rickets among children, due chiefly to wrong feeding. Otherwise conditions were essentially the same; there were the tuberculous patients to be taught the importance of fresh air, nourishing food and hygienic habits; the patients who had to be helped to find new work when illness incapacitated them from the old; surgical implements to be secured and convalescent treatments arranged for those who needed them. In Leeds, too, as in London, there were patients who thronged out-patient departments, going from one hospital to another and getting a bottle of medicine at each, or going from one hospital to another in order to get acceptable advice. But in Leeds, where the three hospitals were under the care of one almoner, such patients were apt to have the disconcerting experience of being interviewed by the very lady who had heard the same—or perhaps even a different—tale the day before. This was the kind of case that tended to convert even the most doubting medical men into at least a temporary belief in the value of an almoner.

Before the outbreak of war, Leeds had recognized the value of the almoner's work, and the department had been accepted as a part of the normal hospital organization. The movement had spread beyond Leeds. In 1913 Miss Becket, who had been Miss Mudd's assistant in Leeds, went on to the Royal Victoria Infirmary, Newcastle-on-Tyne, and found on the medical staff doctors who had worked in London with almoners and had no doubt whatever of their value to the hospital. Here, therefore, there was no battle to fight. Miss Becket was welcomed and enjoyed the felicity of not being obliged to make history.

While the country generally was coming to believe in the value of the trained almoner, Birmingham decided that common sense and goodwill were the only qualifications necessary, and appointed an untrained woman. When in 1912 experience proved to the Governors of the hospital the error of their judgement, they invited the Council of Almoners to train for them Gertrude Humpidge, a student at the Social Service Centre connected with the hospital. The Council had fixed thirty-two as the maximum age for a trainee. Gertrude Humpidge was in her middle forties, and had not the academic qualifications usually demanded. The Council, however, generally so unyielding, felt this to be a special case and sent her to St. Thomas's, where she speedily proved that no mistake had been made in the selection. The work was made more difficult at Birmingham by the fact that the untrained woman had left behind her a certain atmosphere of suspicion; local charitable organizations did not come forward eager to help; people of goodwill waited to see how things shaped before offering their services; the hospital was cautious; it had made one mistake and hoped it had not made another. It was for Gertrude Humpidge to prove this. The Board was willing to give her time, but not to spend much money in establishing this proof. The new almoner therefore found herself without either paid or voluntary help, and since there was an office to be organized, a system of keeping records to institute and a great deal of correspondence to undertake, as well as the interviewing and visiting, which were the essence of the matter, she had more than enough to do. But she was stout-hearted and her wisdom, her imperturbable good humour and her indomitable determination prevailed. It was not long before she had established in Birmingham the sound conviction as to the importance of an almoner's department in any hospital.

It was eminently satisfactory that wherever almoners were employed they proved their value, whether the process of proof was slow or rapid, no hospital, which had had one, was prepared to do without. But this was not enough. There were still far too many hospitals which were not yet willing to make the experiment; far too few educated women who realized the possibilities in the work and a certain suspicion on the part of subscribers to hospital funds that the good money they gave for the sick was possibly being used to pay salaries to young women who should be managing their own homes. It was the part of the Council of Almoners to combat all the ignorance and prejudice which hindered the development of the work.

CHAPTER VII

The Enlightenment of the Public

◆━━━◆

'*The treatment of patients is slovenly without some knowledge of their homes, finances, thoughts and worries.*'

DR. CABOT, U.S.A.

The work of the Council of Almoners was primarily educative. The profession was new. Its usefulness was little known and less appreciated. If it was to be soundly established it was necessary first to attract educated women, convincing them that here was a career interesting and useful; secondly, it was necessary to convince Hospital Boards and the medical profession generally that they could not carry on their work without almoners; and finally, it was necessary to educate the public, who paid the bill, to believe that it was being asked to pay for something infinitely worth while.

The enlightenment of educated women was the easiest of the tasks to tackle. The higher education of women had changed the attitude of society to the sex; a girl was no longer required to preserve her gentility by waiting idly till matrimony should claim her. Educated women were seeking admission to many professions and it was important to direct their attention to that of the Almoner. In 1909, the Council was affiliated to the National Union of Women Workers, bringing itself into line with other women's professions and it gladly accepted the invitation to send a speaker to the Annual Conference of the Union at York, and again in 1913 at Bristol. In each case Anne Cummins was sent. Her speeches, though admirable to read, were sadly disappointing in delivery. For a woman of her experience she was surprisingly shy and diffident and the fact that she was short-sighted and needed to refer to her notes a good deal, was very hampering. But she often came alive and became herself in the questions after her speech, and her wisdom and humanity were so apparent that she made an effect which mere eloquence could not have produced.

In 1911 the Heads of Women's Colleges were invited to join the Council and thus the bonds were drawn closer between the profession and the centres from which its members must increasingly come. When candidates were forthcoming it was the responsibility of the Council to select those who were suitable and to arrange for their training. Here, in spite of its urgent need, the Council moved very cautiously. In 1907, of thirty-four candidates it accepted only ten; it retained always the right to discontinue the training of any candidate who, in its opinion, proved unsuitable. The content and method of the training was the subject of long and careful thought. The Council felt it must be based on a course of general social science supplemented by training in the technique of almoning. The question of the right training for a social worker had exercised Charles Loch's mind long before the first almoner was appointed. In 1899, co-operating

with the Settlements and other philanthropic bodies, the
C.O.S. organized a conference with representatives from
the Universities to consider the possibility of establishing
Social Science courses in some university. The idea was
not well received and it is interesting to notice that the
Universities affirmed that their function was to promote
the pursuit of knowledge for its own sake; they had evi-
dently not then learned that their true function is to 'turn
out' technicians or business executives! The C.O.S. thereupon set up a special committee to consider the training
of social workers. It intended something much more
serious than equipping candidates for a job; its members
believed whole-heartedly that the cause of social reform
depended very largely on an enlightened public opinion
and it endeavoured to plan a course which might usefully
be attended by the clergy, by those who had time to give
to voluntary social work, as well as by those seeking a
training for some specific job. As a result of these efforts
the School of Sociology was founded in 1903, and continued until in 1911, owing to financial difficulties, it was
absorbed by the London School of Economics. Throughout these years it gave serious courses in social and industrial history, economics, the Poor Law and kindred subjects. Practical work was undertaken at Settlements and
in the C.O.S. offices, where it was strongly insisted that
the student was not to be used as an extra office boy, but
made to study each case in relation to local conditions. A
certificate from this School of Sociology or some recognized equivalent was required to admit a candidate to the
training as an almoner, and from 1907, on the conclusion
of this training, the Council awarded a diploma giving
professional status to those who held it.

There was no difficulty in placing these qualified women. The Council used the more experienced members of the profession—Edith Mudd or Anne Cummins—to try out the newly qualified, to assess their suitability to the particular hospital asking for them. With the demand in excess of the supply, it was able to give preference to those hospitals whose Boards were prepared to give real support to the woman appointed.

To increase the number of these co-operative Hospital Boards was the second educative task of the Council. The difficulty was primarily financial; all hospitals were always hard up and any new item of expense was scrutinized with anxiety. The Almoners' Council Report for 1910–11 records dolefully 'There appears to be a certain amount of hesitation on the part of some Hospital Boards to incur the expenses of an almoner's department, though they realize the value of the work. It can be truly said that work of this kind is as necessary to the real efficiency of the hospital as, for instance, the supply of good drugs, and that increased efficiency is worth paying for. Experience has shown that the work done by a trained and qualified almoner may become the basis of a successful appeal on behalf of the hospital.' In their efforts to convince the Boards of the soundness of this view, the almoners had allies in those doctors who had worked with them and appreciated the value of their contribution. The Council invited five of the great London Hospitals to send representatives to sit with it and this greatly strengthened its influence. The *British Medical Journal* published an informative article about the work of the Northcote Trust. Interest was greatly stimulated by the arrival in this country of Dr. Cabot from the Massachusetts General

Hospital at Boston. Dr. Cabot was doing in the States what Loch had done in England; he was a convinced believer in the value of social service in hospitals and was delighted to see at St. Thomas's the system he was trying to introduce into his own hospital work. The difference in the conditions in London and Boston were significant. In Boston there was no tangle of ancient, ill-administered charities to clear away; no over-crowded out-patients' departments to be purged. Dr. Cabot came to the conclusion, simply as a medical practitioner, not as a social reformer, that the hospital could not treat its patients adequately without considering each in his social setting, and that to arrive at an understanding of this required a trained social worker. The expression of this point of view was very valuable to the English almoners, for it stressed the positive, constructive side of the work which was, of course, its real justification. This way of looking at the work spread and the Council felt it had reason for solid satisfaction when, at the Annual Meeting of the British Hospitals' Association at Newcastle in 1913, one of the local surgeons read a paper, in the course of which he said that 'co operation between the doctor and the social worker is absolutely necessary if their common ideals —the raising of the standard of public health and the extermination of disease—are to be realized'.

But the most formidable task remained—the education of those who held the purse strings. The great majority of those who subscribed to the upkeep of hospitals did so through the Hospital Saturday and Sunday Funds, or through the King Edward Hospital Fund, and the Committees of these Funds inevitably exercised great influence on hospital spending. It was therefore very important for

93

those who believed in the work of almoners to persuade them that it was legitimate to spend money on this work. This was not easy, for the Committees were rightly very sensitive to public opinion; those who had given the money obviously had a right to a voice in its disposal. At first every subscriber received 'letters' in numbers proportionate to the magnitude of his subscription, which he could hand out to any protégé and which carried the right to hospital treatment. It was not difficult to show that this system was most unlikely to ensure that those who most needed hospital treatment got it, and the almoners from the beginning protested against it. But it died hard; subscribers were tenacious of their rights and the promoters of the Fund protested that unless subscribers got something for their money, subscriptions would fall off. In 1911 the Council of the King Edward Fund appointed a special committee to enquire into the whole question of the administration of out-patients' departments; it invited the Almoners' Council to give evidence. The Council gladly availed itself of the opportunity, and read with delight the Recommendation of the Committee that 'The adoption of the Almoner system is the first step in the reform of the out-patients' departments'. This seemed —and actually proved—too good to be true, for at the following Annual General Meeting of the Fund this Recommendation was accepted 'in principle', but it was decided 'In view of the uncertainty of the position of hospitals in connection with the National Insurance Act, that no steps could then be taken to carry it out'. It was a disappointing conclusion, but something was gained, for the value of the almoner had been publicly affirmed and to everyone connected with hospitals it was known that the

Insurance Act, whatever its value, made the work of the almoner more rather than less, necessary.

So things remained till the outbreak of the First World War brought new complications into the life and work of every citizen.

CHAPTER VIII

The First World War and the Campaign Against Tuberculosis

'*If preventible, why not prevented?*'

H.M. KING GEORGE V

The war, indeed, as Anne Cummins said, 'burst like a huge earthquake destroying men's habits of life and thought'. No one too young to have experienced it can imagine the shock of incredulity with which the nation discovered itself to be at war. There was first bewilderment, then anger and then an immense and genuine enthusiasm for a cause which was recognized as a stand against tyranny. It was only the more thoughtful who perceived, with Sir Edward Grey, that the beginning of the war was the end of the world they had known. Every institution in the country was shaken out of its accustomed life—hospitals with the rest—and in the hospitals no department was more deeply affected than the Almoners' since its work was to deal with social problems, and these, all over the country, were changing with startling rapidity. In the account which follows of the re-adjustment of the profession to the new conditions, reference is made chiefly to the work at St. Thomas's, not only because it was more fully organized there than elsewhere, but also because the records of that hospital have survived the bombing of two wars and can therefore still be consulted.

The immediate result of the war was to increase the volume, rather than to change the character of, the work. St. Thomas's at once offered 300 beds to the War Office and this involved the discharge of civilians in early stages of convalescence. The arrangements for these necessarily fell upon the almoners; it entailed extensive visiting to determine which patients could reasonably be looked after at home and which must be found accommodation elsewhere. Numbers of private houses were offered as convalescent homes; it was perhaps natural and certainly inconvenient that in most cases there was eagerness to receive casualties and a reluctance to accommodate mere civilians. When the first batch of casualties arrived, almoners found themselves even busier than before; there were all the usual things to do, financial worries to dispel, emotional tangles to unravel, letters to write; and in addition to these customary jobs there was the duty of finding lodgings for the relatives of seriously wounded men whose homes were far from London.

The call up of many civilians into the armed forces added to the strain on the almoners. The wives were dependent on their separation allowances and, considering the numbers involved it is not surprising that there was often much delay in getting these through, so that there was a great call on charitable help to tide over the interval. But gradually Lambeth became prosperous. Most of the hospital patients came normally from the unskilled or semi-skilled classes and the men were mostly in casual labour. Now that they were in the army, the wives received separation allowances; these were not over-generous and the wife of a skilled artisan found herself worse off than she had been. But for the wife of an un-skilled or casual worker the allowances were not only larger than she had been wont to receive but they were also regular and these women found themselves better off than they had ever been. Moreover the war had excited great generosity in the hearts of those who had no active participation in it and a profusion of funds had been started; money was spontaneously given and almost as spontaneously distributed. All this worried Miss Cummins. It was true that the encouragement of thrift had been ex-punged from the list of 'duties' laid upon the almoner, but she could not so easily dismiss it from her mind; she noted that the women with money to spare paid off arrears of rent and then, having become independent of the dreaded landlord, they spent what was left on extrava-gances. Anne Cummins was a realist and could not help knowing that war is destructive and cannot fail to bring poverty. She foresaw the time when wages would fall, unemployment increase and poverty come once more to Lambeth.

As the war went on, the care of discharged soldiers became another duty. The business of helping disabled men to readjust themselves to civilian life was one of the most difficult and important things to be done. It was not different in kind from the work the almoners had been doing for years with patients, who by sickness or misfor-tune had become incapable of the work they had always done, but it was more difficult. There were so many cases and the suddenness of the blow, which had deprived these young men in the full flush of their youth of the skills and powers on which they had always lived, made their rehabilitation a formidable task. There was another element in the problem. For a disabled soldier to get work of a kind was only too easy, at least while the war lasted and labour was short. There was a general readiness to help those who had played their part in the field, and it was fatally easy to find unskilled light work which offered the alluring prospect of prosperity without exaggerated effort. Miss Cummins worked incessantly to get the men who came to St. Thomas's into some skilled employment out of which a new and satisfactory life could be built. There were various Government training schemes and she was closely in touch with the committees which ran them. At one time Clerkenwell Polytechnic had training courses and suitable patients were encouraged to attend these, the Northcote Trust producing the money for their fares and other necessary expenses. Great were the rejoicings in the Hospital when one of their patients came top in an examination. There were other things to be done for these discharged men. The interpretation of Government papers, the correct filling in of forms, the discovery of one's rights and the right way to claim them is not always crystal clear even to those who are familiar with the written word and the involved constructions of official English. To a great many of these discharged men, some of whom could read and others who had learned the art but rarely practised it, the documents handed to them might as well have been written in Hebrew or Greek. It was to the almoners that these documents were brought and as the months went by and directives and forms multiplied, by perseverance and hard work they mastered the language and became efficient interpreters.

The war had the important result of very greatly accleerating social reforms. The more thoughtful part of the public had long been aware of and troubled by the poverty and the deplorable housing conditions in which too many citizens were compelled to live, but there were also far too many smug comfortable people, ready to believe that the working class 'liked it that way', failing to perceive that this, if true, was an indictment of the education which the State had provided. It was perhaps, as much as anything, the introduction of compulsory military service, which shook this complacency. When all men of military age were called to the colours and a large proportion was relegated to the C.3 category after medical examination, the general public began to ask if Britain could really be becoming a C.3 nation and to demand that something should be done about it. Both Central and Local Authority were moved. The prevalence of tuberculosis was taken seriously. There were not nearly enough sanatoria. The Insurance Act had provided for insured persons, but not for their dependants or for the uninsured. Far too little educative work to prevent the spread of the disease was being done. To many people the fact that the disease was preventible came as a surprise and when the King asked: 'If preventible, why not prevented?' he was expressing the view of many of his subjects, who had hitherto given the matter no thought.

Now, however, a serious effort was made to cope with the disease; local authorities took over the responsibility. St. Thomas's had already shown the way to tackle this problem and the President of the Local Government

Board had the good sense to seek help from those experienced in the work. He spent long hours with Miss Cummins in the office of the Northcote Trust, looking at its records, studying its methods and discussing every detail with the visitors. And it was on these consultations that he based the regulations issued to local authorities.

As early as 1916 the London County Council had constituted 'Interim Committees' to deal with the tuberculous in London. These of course presented a certain problem to the Northcote Trust, which dealt with all the St. Thomas's patients irrespective of the borough from which they came, whereas the L.C.C. committees were organized regionally. The question then arose as to whether Northcote workers must hand over those patients who did not live in Lambeth, to the care of the L.C.C., or retain them, in spite of the new scheme. There could be no doubt which of these alternatives the patients would prefer; it was a choice between being helped by friends or by officials; between receiving such financial relief as was needed, at the discretion of one who knew all the personal issues involved, or from a visitor, who however friendly, was bound by regulation and could only give in circumstances which could be squeezed into a recognized category. But as Miss Cummins perceived, there was an issue at stake more important than the treatment of these individual cases. The whole future treatment of tuberculous patients depended on a right and uniform organization of the work and, this being so, she regretfully decreed that all patients except those in Lambeth must be handed over to their local committees. The Lambeth Interim Committee allowed the Northcote worker to continue to look after all the cases in that borough and invited a representative of the Trust to sit with it. This supersession of a private charitable work by public authority is of course inevitable; it has happened in education, in medicine and in every sort of social work. There is gain and there is loss. The gain is that a service available only to the few becomes available to all; the loss consists in the substitution of an official service, bound by regulation, for a friendly personal relationship which makes possible the adjustment of the service offered to meet the infinitely varied needs of the individual.

Another product of the war was a greatly quickened sensibility to the needs of children; perhaps it was partly the ever increasing lists of casualties, the thought of the hundreds of young lives cut short that made the young lives springing up seem doubly precious. Baby centres and ante-natal clinics, baby welcomes and every sort of mothercraft centre sprang up all over the country. The part already played by St. Thomas's in this movement has already been recorded. Here again the President of the Local Government Board consulted Miss Cummins and the maternity department of the Hospital, when he made his plans. In 1916, in accordance with its policy of working with public authorities, the Hospital made an arrangement by which all St. Thomas's babies, less than a year old, who had bronchitis, applied to the district nurses for help. As a result there was no pneumonia and no death among these patients, a fact mentioned with commendation in the Local Government Board's report on infant mortality for the year 1915–16.

The almoner's work went on the lines it had pursued from the beginning, but of course there was much more of it. Ceaselessly they tried to get children properly fed, but the provision of milk—though it cost only 5d. a quart—was beyond the financial reach of many families. The provision of cots and suitable clothes was an easier matter, though there was a very general scepticism as to the importance of nether garments; however, when parcels began to arrive from America and Australia, containing knitted woollen knickers, these became fashionable in Lambeth and much to be desired. Even with the clothing problem solved the almoners found much to do for the families. It was a difficult time. The absence of fathers and of teachers in boys' schools, the war atmosphere of excitement and anxiety in which they lived tended to loosen the bonds of discipline and to disintegrate the family, and distracted mothers constantly sought the advice of the almoner.

It had always been part of the almoner's work to encourage fathers also to concern themselves with the new baby, coming or come, and in 1916, with the active encouragement of the doctors at St. Thomas's, Miss Cummins devised an important innovation. This was an evening session every week in the study of the Rector of Lambeth, at which every husband, not overseas, of every woman whose baby was to be born in the Hospital, met the doctor who was attending the case. This was a wonderful experience both for the doctor and for the father, more especially for the latter, but the doctor gained something too; an insight into a very important part of his patient's environment and a better understanding than he could otherwise have gained of the outlook of the ordinary uneducated Englishman. The father's gain is obvious; a new understanding of an experience which he had hitherto ignored as altogether the wife's affair and one which need make no demands on him. This scheme, hatched in Miss Cummins's fertile mind, was one of her most notable contributions to the family life of St. Thomas's patients.

The Club for Mothers was also a very happy institution. It met in a small house near the Hospital. Mothers came with their children who were taken by voluntary workers into another room and entertained with suitable toys and occupations, while the mothers enjoyed a good gossip and a cup of really 'good' tea. The club was immensely uncomfortable and immensely popular. In 1918 the mothers asked that their husbands should be allowed to become members with them of the club; this request was at once granted and the club became even more over-crowded and by any ordinary standard, uncomfortable, but it also became increasingly popular. No one was really surprised when the Local Authority condemned the house and ordered its demolition. This naturally increased the enthusiasm of the members for their club and the Northcote Trustees came to the rescue by finding a better and more convenient house, with space enough to separate small children from the larger ones and still leave room for the parents. Members and their friends were proud to contribute according to their means and the club continued to flourish.

One feature of war-time London could not fail to distress any thoughtful observer. This was the plight of the young girl. The gynaecological department was thronged with girls who were in danger, through syphilis, of being incapacitated not only from work but also from future motherhood. For these girls Anne Cummins felt the deepest compassion. 'In many cases,' she writes, 'craving for excitement, love of dress and what for her represents her ideals of beauty and enjoyment leads a girl into danger and she awakens to despair.' London was no easy place for a working girl; the presence of so many men, the darkness of the streets, the horror and excitement of war all tended to make a callow and emotional girl believe that this was the one chance she was likely to get of having 'a good time'. It was easy enough to see how the situation had arisen; Anne Cummins's problem was how it should be met. It was a very general view that the girl should be returned to her own family if she had one, and get the treatment she needed at the hospital nearest to her home. This seemed to Miss Cummins a counsel of despair. Very often a girl's home was most unlikely to be able to help, for it was probably an undisciplined home life and an unfortunate temperament, very likely inherited, which had made the resistance to temptation too difficult; sending them home was simply taking a risk, not only for the girl but for those with whom she was likely to associate. Miss Cummins's first step, therefore, was to make a careful register of all the cases, in order to make sure that no girl should cease attending hospital till her treatment was completed and she had ceased to be a source of infection. She got into touch with the rescue and welfare workers in the girl's district and worked closely with the clergy. But this was only a *pis aller*; it might and no doubt did help the easier sort of case, the girl who had made one mistake and had repudiated it with her will. For the majority, for the weak, who lacked the courage of resolution to make a fresh start; for those who had practised prostitution and, having thought to abandon it when frightened by disease, being cured, turned to it again;

for these something more fundamental was needed.

This problem was never out of Anne Cummins's mind and when in 1919 a generous donor offered the Northcote Trust a large house with a garden, quite near the hospital, she saw that here was the opportunity she had so long desired. The house, called Northcote House, was opened on 1st January 1920 as a hostel for selected patients from the gynaecological department. It could accommodate fourteen girls and some six babies. The matron was left entirely free from red tape. It was she, together with the almoner, who selected the girls and these were chosen simply on the grounds that they seemed to be genuinely anxious to make a fresh start and to have some degree of moral stamina to make this possible. The length of each girl's stay depended simply on her need. Within the hostel life was pretty strenuous. All the domestic work in the house was done by the girls and they were taught to do it properly. A high standard of efficiency was expected; they were taught domestic arts and mothercraft; nor was their cultural education overlooked. Talks on current events, visits to exhibitions, galleries, the theatre and the cinema were arranged and the house was made gay and beautiful with light colours and always a good supply of flowers. For Anne Cummins, keenly alive to beauty, felt it to be a very important influence on the young. There were failures, of course; some of the very young, who had neither at home nor at school learned to accept discipline, needed a longer and more intensive training than North-cote House could give. For these children the only hope lay in persuading them voluntarily to go into a recognized training school and it will readily be believed that few of them could be persuaded to accept so drastic a remedy.

Others seemed to respond and no doubt intended to do so, but as the weeks went by in a steady job, they would suddenly revolt against the intolerable monotony of regular work and go back into the life from which they had been rescued. But there were successes too; girls who managed to make the immense effort to hold to the standards they had acquired at the hostel and came back joyfully to ask advice, to report progress, to boast of success. It is reported of one girl that she asked permission to come back to Northcote House to spend the night before her wedding there, for to her it had been truly a home. The contribution which Northcote House was able to make to the whole moral problem of London's streets was of course infinitesimal, but people are not reformed *en masse*. Even a small handful of girls put in the way of living a full and happy life is a matter for congratulation. It cost a good deal, financially, but whenever the Trust appealed for extra funds for the hostel they came from those glad to contribute in however small a degree to a problem of overpowering dimensions.

The problem is still with us, though its character has altered. Northcote House was bombed in the last war, and when it was rebuilt it was unanimously agreed that it could no longer be serviceable as a hostel since medical science has produced new drugs which obviate the necessity of long treatments, so there is no opportunity for the re-education of patients. Other methods must be found, since cities and societies are not cleansed by legislation or by penal measures, however enlightened, but only by the conversion of their members and this can only be achieved individual by individual—there is no short cut.

CHAPTER IX

Post-War Problems

◆━━━━━◆

> '*Each generation must find its own way through its own difficulties.*'
>
> OCTAVIA HILL

B y the time Northcote House was opened, peace, so ardently desired, so dearly paid for, had come. Through the weary war years men had sought comfort in thinking of the 'Brave new world' which their efforts should establish. Politicians had indeed promised 'Homes fit for Heroes', a world safe for democracy and war damage paid for by the Kaiser who had caused it. Inevitably, peace must bring prosperity. In fact the world was quite different. Europe lay in ruins and everybody had to pay. Homes, which owing to shortage of labour had not been kept in repair, were unfit for quite ordinary people and, since building had practically ceased through the war, there were far too few of them. The birthrate had risen and overcrowding was acute. All schools were full; there were not enough teachers to cope with the children and there were problems of discipline due partly at least to the general disorganization of life during the war. The extinction of capital and the poverty of those

countries which had been among our best customers led
to a loss of trade and this brought unemployment and all
the suffering it must entail. The bitterness of disillusion-
ment was proportionate to the exaggerated hopes which
had been indulged in and the period between the wars
was one of great discontent and unrest.

This bitter, difficult world presented a challenge to all
social workers and obliged them to reflect upon the
adequacy of the resources at their disposal. The almoners
found these far from satisfactory. Theirs had never been a
self-governing profession. The Almoners' Council, which
was responsible for the recruitment and training of candidates for the profession, was an off-shoot of the Charity
Organization Society, to which the working almoners
elected first one and later two representatives. This could
not be satisfactory to the practitioners of any profession;
that it worked at all was due partly to the very real
wisdom and understanding of Charles Loch, partly to the
fact that the almoners on the Council were women of ex-
ceptional force and ability, who exercised an influence out
of proportion to their number.

The working almoners had made themselves into a
committee to 'discuss the possibilities and difficulties of
the work'. They met pleasantly, informally; they elected
no officers; from time to time they passed resolutions as
to procedure and in 1912 they agreed to invite all certificated almoners to join them. Hitherto the Committee had
consisted of the twenty Head Almoners. The addition of
the assistants raised their membership to thirty. The subscription was small but in 1914, finding themselves in
possession of a balance of £4, alarmed at so great an
accumulation of wealth, they spent it on books, thus

forming the nucleus of the Institute Library of today; and they halved the subscription.

But a changed world clearly demanded some less nebulous organization and in 1920 the Association of Hospital Almoners was formally constituted and was affiliated to the Federation of Professional Social Workers. Two years later the Council of Almoners was also reconstituted and was incorporated as the Institute of Hospital Almoners. This was an important step in the development of the profession, for in the new Constitution it was emancipated from the control of the Charity Organization Society. A third of the members of the Institute were to be elected annually by the Association from its members and the remaining two-thirds were to represent, not only the C.O.S. but also such other bodies as Governing Boards and the Medical Staffs of Hospitals, the local Almoners' Committees and other interested bodies. This arrangement put the affairs of the profession very much more clearly into the hands of those who were actively engaged in the work. The Institute retained responsibility for the selection and training of candidates for the profession and its income was derived from fees paid by students for their training. This very soon proved insufficient, for the Institute was also responsible not only for placing qualified almoners in jobs, but also for the organization of meetings and for all the publicity required to make the work more generally known. When this situation was put to the Association it was really agreed that a contribution from the funds of the Association should be paid to the Institute. The Institute and the Association worked far more closely together than had been possible before; subjects for discussion were passed from one to the other and conferences were held to the great advantage of the whole profession.

Conferences were indeed playing a very large part in the social development of these post-war years; where conditions were so difficult and problems so complex, discussions among those concerned in them could not fail to be productive. It was becoming more clearly seen that all social work, whether concerned with health, education, housing, or general poverty was essentially one and that for any body to work in isolation was simply stupid. Conference houses were opened in various parts of the country and the almoners organized their first week-end conference at High Leigh in 1924. This was so successful that it became an annual event in co-operation with various other social organizations, each society in turn acting as host. Distinguished speakers from outside the societies were invited to attend and address the conference and these week-ends proved both stimulating and refreshing to those taking part in them.

In 1924 Anne Cummins and Phyllis Lyall of Glasgow were invited to represent the Association of Almoners at the Annual General Meeting of Social Workers of America. They went to Boston, where they already had friends in Dr. Cabot and Miss Cannon of the General Hospital of Massachusetts and then went to Toronto for the Annual Meeting, where Miss Cummins was the principal speaker at the Annual Dinner. It was an interesting conference and as they talked they discovered, almost with surprise, that though conditions in England and America differed widely, and though medical social workers in the two countries had approached their problems from entirely different directions, yet the ideals and methods which had evolved in the two countries were almost identical. This visit was a very important land-mark and the starting point of the two-way traffic of social workers going to America and of American social workers coming here. Miss Cummins always set great store by this experience and urged anyone to go who could possibly manage it. At considerable cost to her own health she stayed on at St. Thomas's for a longer period to enable her successor, Cherry Morris, to visit the U.S.A. before starting at the Hospital and in the same way Miss Read, who followed Miss Morris, went for a few months to the U.S.A. before taking up her job.

In 1927 the first International Conference of Social Workers took place; it was held in Paris and delegates came from every part of the Continent as well as from America and Great Britain. Here again was a most stimulating experience and here national characteristics were amusingly apparent; the Russians were clear that no really useful social work was possible under a capitalist system; the French that national idiosyncracies were so marked that no country could usefully attempt to learn from the methods of others; the Germans that the root of the matter lay in keeping orderly and careful records. The London County Council Medical Officer of Health read a long paper about the excellence of its dealings with schoolchildren in clinics and health centres, which it declared to be unique. But he was followed by a speaker from Greece, who revealed that the Greek system was practically identical! The veteran Dr. Cabot was present and delighted the English delegation by giving as his considered opinion that the system of training for almoners devised in England was the best in the world.

This approval by so distinguished an authority was of course most gratifying, but it could not compensate the almoners for the fact that all too few women were being admitted to this admirable training. During the war years this had been natural enough; there was much work to be done more directly connected with the forces and therefore more attractive. With the end of the war, as women came out of the forces and were offered grants from various sources to enable them to train for civilian work, the position ought rapidly to have improved. Actually, in 1920 there were only fifty-one qualified almoners. The Institute had not been supine during the war; it had realized the importance of securing candidates for the future. In 1917 it had commissioned Anne Cummins with Mrs. Thomas who, as Molly Verrall, had been her first assistant, to undertake a publicity campaign in the northern university towns. They visited Leeds, Liverpool, Newcastle and Glasgow and addressed the hospital authorities, women's colleges and employment agencies in these towns, expounding the value of the work to be done and the opportunity it offered to an educated woman for a satisfying professional career. The expedition aroused great interest in the centres visited and Miss Cummins was invited in the following year to go again to Liverpool to address the Annual Meeting of the National Union of Women Workers. As a result of these visits, the Institute considered the possiblity of arranging training schemes outside the Metropolis. Most universities offered a course in social science, generally with a certain amount of practical work done in connection with the local Settlements. In 1919 the Institute arranged with Leeds University a scheme to add to the existing social science courses material necessary to almoners and authorized Leeds General Infirmary to give the practical training. The Institute, however, insisted that all applications for training must be made through London and that the Training Committee there should have the power to accept or reject them. It is no uncommon idea among those who live outside the Metropolis that Londoners have a quite unjustified opinion of their own importance and capacity and many of those working in the north, in Leeds particularly, resented this assumption of authority by the Institute. These almoners were convinced that a number of suitable candidates were prevented from coming forward because they could not afford the expense of training in London; and they believed that local training schemes could tap new resources. In Leeds the position of the almoners was strong. They had always had the steady support of the Chairman of the Hospital Board, and of local public opinion. A local committee was therefore formed which put to the Institute a proposition for the establishment of a Selection and Training Committee in Leeds.

In 1926, after some discussion, it was agreed that Leeds should have such a Committee and that all students whether admitted in Leeds or in London, should do part of their practical training in London and part in the provinces. The result of this development was fully justified in Leeds, which secured a small but steady stream of candidates for the profession; but it was not as decisive as had been hoped, and the shortage remained a serious problem.

There was, no doubt, a variety of reasons for this shortage and it may be that the Selection Committee was over-cautious in its acceptance of candidates. Selection is seldom easy. Octavia Hill, talking of the training of the Woman Property Manager, had said, 'There are some things she must know, but whether she will succeed depends, not on what she knows, but on what she is.' This is true, and applies equally to any sort of social worker. Unfortunately, while it is easy to discover with a reasonable degree of accuracy what a candidate knows, what she is remains far less ascertainable and in the end the judgement will be subjective; the Committee could only say that in its opinion the candidate was 'Not suitable' for the work. It is obvious that such a judgement would not commend itself to the candidate, nor would it be easily accepted by her friends. To the critics of the Committee it seemed that the rejection was often made on social grounds. The post-war generation suffered from an almost pathological horror of snob values. The very name of 'Lady Almoner' was objectionable and its innocent historical origin no excuse; there was no getting away from the fact that in the early days, Loch and the founders of the profession had insisted on the importance of selecting the almoner from a class superior to those whom she was to serve. Here again a very small degree of historical sense might have saved a great deal of indignation. In an age, when there was a really wide gap between the educated and the working class, when the latter, by reason of ignorance and poverty, was unable to defend or express itself, it was supremely important that those to be appointed to advise and help should be possessed of the wide outlook and sensitive understanding which should come with education and is very unlikely to be developed without it. In an age, when there was very little to call education for any outside the leisured classes, it was inevitable that these should provide the almoners. By the mid-twenties the social structure had changed considerably, but it was still necessary to select candidates of the same calibre as those of the earlier days. It was perhaps less easy to distinguish them. It may be that the Committee rejected some who might have made admirable almoners; no committee is infallible. No doubt the rejected were convinced that it constantly failed. At one point the suggestion was made that the Institute should accept all applicants and that the ultimate authority for admission or rejection should be vested in those who trained them. This plan, however, was not adopted. It would inevitably entail waste of time for the rejected candidate; considerable disorganization of the almoners' department; and would add a very distasteful duty to the almoner obliged to reject a well-meaning but unsuitable colleague.

There were other reasons for the shortage of almoners. The position of the profession was not really secure. Women doctors, women secretaries and nurses had been practising for so long that they had been universally accepted; for almoners it was different. Many hospitals were only partly convinced of the value of their work. What more likely than that a Hospital Board, harried by mounting expenses, should determine that the almoners' department was a suitable place for retrenchment?

The difficulties of the years between the wars, not only in this country but throughout the world, were fundamentally economic. War is extravagant and the impoverishment which follows is made more difficult to cope with by the habit, acquired during the war, of pouring out money lavishly, since in a life and death struggle mere money seems deceptively unimportant. Every institution found itself confronted by new problems for which it was necessary to find new solutions. It is probable that every organization thought its own difficulties more acute than those of any other body; certainly the voluntary hospitals found theirs grievous. They had always depended on voluntary subscriptions and these were now seriously diminished; for money was changing hands and it was just those whose tradition and training had given them a sense of obligation to charitable institutions who were suffering from smaller incomes. Moreover taxation was high—not of course high judged by present standards but higher than it had ever been—and since some of the money thus demanded went to the relief of the sick poor, it seemed fair enough, to those who anxiously scrutinized their pass books, to cut down on the hospital subscription. The voluntary hospitals, though they were given grants for special purposes by local authorities, got nothing from the Exchequer, so to them their steadily falling income was a serious matter. Moreover, the costs of running a hospital were steadily rising. It was not only that every item—wages, repairs, maintenance and drugs—cost more, but also that the public rightly demanded a much higher level of health in the community. The medical profession had acquired new techniques and new skills in dealing with those physical infirmities which had hitherto been accepted as inevitable. It is a significant fact that the hospital once known as the 'Hospital for Incurable Children', repudiating the adjective 'incurable' as applicable to children, became the 'Victoria Hospital for Children'. The child who, a generation earlier, had been allowed to wilt into an early, and if fiction is to be believed, an edifying grave, must now be treated, given the food and exercises that would enable him to grow into a normal member of society—a consummation entirely to be desired, but also, to the hospital, expensive.

With this situation—a falling income and rising expenditure—no hospital could continue on the old lines and in recognition of this fact an Act of Parliament was passed in 1920, which authorized voluntary hospitals to make some charge to their patients to defray the cost of their treatment. This at once raised the question as to the basis on which the charge was to be made. It was not to be imagined that contributions from the patients could cover the full cost of treatment. The imposition of a flat rate for everyone, varying according to the length and costliness of the treatment, was almost universally rejected on the grounds that it would put a most unfair burden on the poorest and would very likely prevent his seeking help at the hospital until it was too late to be effective. The alternative was that every patient should be carefully assessed, consideration being given, not only to his wages but also to his commitments, responsibilities and future earning capacity. This was obviously the fairest plan, but it raised at once the difficult question as to who should make this important and so delicate assessment.

On the face of it the person best qualified to do this was without doubt the almoner. She knew the homes and conditions of her patients, and since they were her friends and trusted her she need not be inquisitorial in her methods, as they were willing enough to discuss their affairs with her. From the point of view of the Hospital Board, which employed an almoner, this conclusion seemed so logical as to be inescapable; to the almoner herself the solution was not so self evident. There were two important considerations. If to the social work she was already doing there was to be added all the administrative work which assessment would involve, would the hospital board be ready to provide and to pay for sufficient administrative staff to allow the almoner still to have time to do her real work, which was to serve the patients? The other question was whether the relation of almoner and patient might be spoiled, the patient's confidence shaken, if an assessment of the contribution was made on the basis of facts given in conversation to the almoner? The answer was not at all simple. Anne Cummins, according to her custom, consulted her staff. She held a meeting with all her St. Thomas's colleagues to consider the situation and to make up their minds whether they were willing to attempt to undertake this business of assessment. The discussion was long and anxious. As Anne Cummins herself saw it, the salient fact was that patients had got to pay something; nobody likes to be asked to pay for what he has previously regarded as a right; what must be decided was whether the patients would find the necessity of paying less painful if the necessary enquiry was made by the almoner rather than by an official specially appointed, who would have to ask questions which the almoner, knowing the facts already, could avoid. Some of the almoners felt that many patients would be obliged to pay more than was just, simply because they could not bear to reveal to a stranger some expensive skeleton in a cupboard of which the almoner already had the key. In the end the St. Thomas's almoners agreed to undertake the assessment of contributions.

At the time this decision seemed right and it was endorsed by the Institute, which minuted the opinion that the almoner was the person most capable of assessing the contributions of patients with justice, and that therefore the work should be entrusted to her. This was all very well for St. Thomas's and for those hospitals which had long employed an almoner and where the character of an almoner's work was thoroughly understood. But in the result the decision had serious consequences, not fully foreseen, for though the Institute had accepted the idea that the almoner should assess the contributions, it was a short step for the less enlightened authorities to require their almoner also to collect these contributions and keep all the records. The situation was complicated by the Poor Law Act of 1928. This removed the functions of the Poor Law from the Local Government Board and empowered local authorities to take over the control of all infirmaries and other institutions which had been controlled by the Guardians. These institutions were no longer to be regarded as the last refuge for the pauper, in which he might be cared for to the end of his life, but as hospitals in which, as in any other, the sick would be medically treated. This new aspect of the Institution presented a challenge to the almoners. If their work was as valuable as they claimed, then they were as essential in these new hospitals as in the old voluntary ones. If local authorities, with their ready command of money, did not think it worth while to employ them, how could it be argued that they had a real function as social workers? For the sake of the profession it was of extreme importance to establish the indispensable nature of the almoner's work to hospital authorities and to the public.

It happened just at this time, as the twenties passed into the thirties, that the strenuous efforts of the Institute to secure more entrants into the profession began to bear fruit and an increasing number of trained and certificated almoners was ready for employment. It was unfortunate that just at this moment hospitals looking for economies were hesitating to offer such employment. For the profession the situation was critical, since its whole future depended on having a steady supply of new entrants. Yet young women contemplating a career in the field of social work could not be expected to embark on the long and exacting course of training demanded for an almoner, if there was known to be unemployment in that profession. Yet, if when the tide turned and hospitals again sought almoners there were no qualified women available, was it not likely that they would employ untrained women and thus destroy a profession capable of serving the best interests of the hospitals and the nation? It seemed therefore necessary, at all costs, to find work for those emerging from their training. The cost was high, but to pay it seemed inevitable. If hospital authorities tended to regard the employment of almoners as an unjustifiable expense, they must be persuaded that, on the contrary, it would be fully worth while. No local authority particularly wants to assess its own patients' capacity to pay, since this does not tend to the popularity of the assessor; and so the suggestion that almoners should do this irksome job commended itself and almoners were appointed to what had been Poor Law Institutions. Qualified almoners were quickly absorbed and after 1932 the demand for them greatly exceeded the supply.

The situation was saved, but in the process something

very important had been lost; this was the clear conception of an almoner's essential function. In the beginning she had been appointed ostensibly to act as a kind of watch dog to prevent exploitation of the hospital, but from the beginning also she had regarded herself as a friend of the patient chiefly concerned in helping him to make full use of the hospital service. As the years went by she had managed to establish her position as one who worked as a colleague of the medical men to help the patients to full recovery and re-adaptation to normal life. It was this conception of the almoners' work which was jeopardized by acceptance of the assessment of payments as part of her duty. Joan Brett was the first almoner to be appointed by public authority; she worked in the General Hospital at Kingston-on-Thames; she found herself obliged to undertake a great deal of clerical work; forms to be filled in, records to be kept, and above all accounts meticulously set out in a form approved by the public auditor. She accepted the necessity for all this and found she could do valuable work acting as a link between the medical and relief departments, but she was spending as much time on administrative as on medical social work.

In the following year Middlesex and London County Councils took over the infirmaries and appointed almoners, but whereas Middlesex appointed them to serve as part of the Health Service, under the Medical Officer of Health, London made them part of the Welfare Service under the Relieving Officer. Thus the emphasis was shifted and the almoner was regarded as valuable, not so much for the help she gave the patients, as for her share in the administration. It is not suggested that this deterioration in the position of the almoner was universal or even very general. In hospitals which had long employed them the tradition was too firmly established to be lost, but even in those hospitals there was the constant danger that the thin edge of the wedge might carry behind it a very large and ugly butt. For in no hospital could this assessing be added to an almoner's duty without very greatly increasing its weight. It did not consist simply in ascertaining from already known patients a few more relevant facts; it involved making contact with every patient and keeping an immensely increased number of records. Unless the Hospital Board was prepared to give extra help in the way of clerical and other assistants, the medical social work could not be done effectively and if the Board had appointed the almoner in the hope of saving money, such a proposition was unlikely to be received with favour.

Unfortunately, there had never been any authoritative pronouncement by the Institute or any other body as to the weight of case load which an almoner could effectively carry. Any matron can say what is the ratio of nurses to patients for the efficient running of a ward in her care; any education officer can say the number of teachers needed to staff a school of given numbers satisfactorily, but no such calculation had ever been made for almoners and the almoner struggling doggedly with reports, accounts and lists found more and more cases being put upon her and had no time to consider whether she could call a halt.

This was a cumulative evil. It is very necessary for anyone who is doing responsible work, which is concerned with people rather than with things, to have time to pause, to look at his particular problem in relation to the whole background, to reflect on fundamental principles, to assure himself as to his destination and his progress. If he is so deeply absorbed in day to day detail that he has no time for this, he inevitably loses the vision and his work becomes flat and unproductive of the highest good. This is what happened to many almoners. There was a danger that, lacking the time to establish the easy friendly relationship with her clients—so important to her work —she might cease to be regarded as a friend—one with leisure to listen, able to interpret official letters and notices, to make it clear what 'They' expected them to do and ready always to help to remove stumbling blocks from a difficult path. She might become rather 'The lady who stamps my card', 'The one who tells you where to go for convalescence'—just a bit of hospital machinery; one of 'Them' in fact, far off like the Olympians and not very much more good than they.

There were of course many almoners who were able to rise above these difficulties and to stand out against the insidious pressure put upon them to abandon their real function, but it was a severe test. Others were not strong enough to face it and accepted a kind of 'maid of all work' position in the hospital. Since the general public is apt to accept its servants at their own valuation, the profession suffered somewhat in public esteem. This was natural enough. The age of the pioneers was past. When there were only seven almoners they were all remarkable women. When there came to be several hundred of them it was not to be expected that they should all be great. Even so Miss Beale and Miss Buss, Dr. Elizabeth Garrett and Sophia Jex Blake were women of unusual capacity whose influence on their contemporaries was wider and more significant than that of the large numbers of competent

124

women who succeeded them in education and medicine. The misfortune for the almoners was that they were engulfed in the social revolution which followed the First World War before they had had time to establish the foundations of the profession so securely that its real value was recognized and its status ensured. And the profession was given no time to recover from the uncertainties of its position before the Second World War came, finding it unable to offer the nation that service which it alone could have given.

CHAPTER X

Expanding Horizons

◆━━━▶

'*The medical staff regard this experiment as a permanency and strongly recommend its adoption in every hospital in the State.*'

DR. COOPER, Medical Superintendent of
Melbourne Hospital, 1930

The profession was developing in many directions. In the late twenties, the subject of mental health and its treatment, based on the theories of Freud, Adler and Jung, was a new and rather exciting preoccupation of the general public. All revolutionary ideas have much the same history. They inspire wild enthusiasm and exaggerated claims and hopes among the more emotional and less intelligent. Each in turn is to be the panacea for all ills. This naturally breeds a reaction among the more conservative thinkers who, in rejecting the exaggerations, are apt to underestimate the value of the idea itself. Meanwhile, its serious exponents continue to work it out undisturbed by popular clamour or conservative distrust. This is what happened with the science of psychology. When in the post-war period psychology burst on the general public as a new science, the Press made much of it. There was a slogan which ran, 'Every man his own laboratory' and many to whom serious study and 'book learning' were temperamentally distasteful, accepted this with delight. For what is more exhilarating than the concentrated study of one's own personality, especially if the blessed word 'complex' provides a satisfactory excuse for any feature not altogether admirable that one may discover?

It was no wonder that a great body of educated people reacted against it. It was Teutonic in origin, it came from America, that land of 'stunts' and most unfortunately this most difficult science, with its delicate and highly complicated technique, was made to sound like a parlour game which anyone might play. Among the unlearned catchwords took the place of principles and there are still parents who will allow their children to scatter litter all over the park because they fear 'to give him a complex, which is so dangerous'.

Confronted with this new departure in the art of healing, the Institute of Almoners moved cautiously. It was clearly neither possible nor desirable that every almoner should be a psychiatrist, yet equally obvious that since, as Professor Hart said, 'More people are ill because they are unhappy than unhappy because they are ill,' some understanding of psychological processes must be of value to the almoner. The Institute took counsel with medical men particularly interested in mental health and arrived at the conclusion that, though at that time there was no demand for almoners in mental hospitals and the neurological departments of general hospitals, yet the need of them was so great that some special training for such work ought to be planned; and that all almoners should have some instruction in psychology.

The Institute was already represented on the Committee of the Child Welfare Council and with the help of this body four qualified almoners, as well as social workers from other fields, were able to get further training at Child Guidance Clinics in the United States of America. The Institute had the help of Dr. Mapother of the Maudsley Hospital, who organized a course for training in mental welfare work for trained almoners; and of the London School of Economics, where a postgraduate course in mental health was set up. By 1930 five almoners had completed the training in mental welfare and were employed in psychiatric social work. A few who had taken American courses and others who had attended those at the London School of Economics came back to work with the almoners, thereby immensely enriching the profession. Others grew impatient at the slow appreciation in some hospitals of the importance of their work, resenting the pressure put upon almoners' departments to undertake an increasing amount of administrative detail, and feeling that, as almoners, they were too much restricted by the conservatism of the medical profession, they preferred to train as psychiatric social workers and work in the psychiatric field, joining the separate social work organization recently set up—the Association of Psychiatric Social Workers. This tended to a division of almoners from psychiatric social workers, a division much regretted by many workers in each field today. Indeed there is less and less reality in it, for the new positive conception of medical science being concerned with health rather than with the cure of disease is bringing together physician and psychiatrist in an effort to deal with the whole personality. Mental disease is no longer in quite a separate compartment and those who are dealing with it, doctors, psychiatrists and social workers, by whatever name they are called, cannot avoid working together.

In another way work developed satisfactorily. Geographically its borders were extending. Almoners were appointed to Cyprus, Stockholm and Paris. Students came for training from Holland and Siam and later from Latvia and Finland; and in 1936 a Medical Officer from Hong Kong, after attending an international conference on social work in England, announced his intention of going back to his hospital and organizing a complete almoners' department there. Government welfare posts were also offered to almoners, a testimony to the value of their training for any sort of social work. Such posts were held in Palestine and Jamaica.

Perhaps the most important extension of the work between the wars took place in the Antipodes. It began in Melbourne in answer not to a plea that out-patients were 'burdensome', nor to satisfy any theory of charitable administration, but because one individual had been brought face to face with an unsatisfied human need. Mrs. Kent Hughes, who was the moving spirit in the matter, has contributed this account:

'I was senior nurse on day duty in the Female Casualty Ward at the time and one day one of the patients, a girl of eighteen, in whom I was interested, failed to attend for treatment. In a pre-penicillin era a septic hand was a more or less serious complaint, therefore her non-attendance caused me deep concern. That evening, when I went off duty, I looked up the patient's address in the Casualty Register and, breaking hospital rules, I collected dressings, antiseptics, surgical instruments, etc., and set forth by train and thence by foot to the outskirts of an industrial suburb to the girl's home to discover for myself just why she had failed to report for treatment.

'I found that during the previous night my patient's mother had died in a sanatorium for tuberculosis victims. Her father, normally a decent sort of chap, had been drinking steadily for some days in a vain attempt to drown his grief in alcohol. When under the influence of liquor he was sullen, quarrelsome and even dangerous. There were eight children all told, the eldest being my eighteen-year-old patient. She burst into tears when she opened the front door and found me standing on the door mat. "I'm sorry, Nurse," she stammered, "but I couldn't leave the children. They are scared of Dad when he gets like this and I am the only one who can handle him." She paused, choked back her sobs and continued. "You see, Nurse, I also had to arrange the burial; interview the undertaker. . . ." At this stage she broke down completely and it was some time before I could comfort her and gently persuade her to let me put fresh dressing on her badly infected hand. "You mustn't judge Dad too hardly, Nurse," she said in parting. "He's a good father when he's sober and I give you my word that as soon as the funeral is over tomorrow I shall report at the hospital."

'It so happened that with the generous co-operation of the Resident Medical Staff, one of the hospital chaplains and the Secretary of the Victorian Charity Organization Society, we were able to render constructive help to this family. The younger children were placed temporarily in a Church Home. The father went as a voluntary inmate to an institution a few miles away from the city, where alcoholics received special treatment; the eighteen-year-old girl being admitted as an in-patient and kept under close supervision until her infectious condition cleared up. She was then given a short holiday at the seaside as the guest of a charitable agency. Subsequently more suitable employment was found for the father and better housing accommodation for them all.'

The nurse, who later became Mrs. Kent Hughes, pondered deeply on this case. She could not fail to realize that this family was not unique and that there must be many families which went under, not because of any real vice nor from any hardness of heart in the community, but simply because they were inarticulate and the public ignorant. Clearly there should be better liaison between hospital patients and the other charitable organizations. For the moment it seemed not possible to do anything, but in 1921 Mrs. Kent Hughes became Secretary of the Melbourne Hospital Auxiliary and in that capacity was able to organize a Social Service Bureau designed to do this work of correlation. At first the Bureau was staffed by voluntary workers, who attended at the Bureau to receive reports and instructions from medical and nursing staff. But as the value of the work proved itself, its volume increased and became beyond the resources of a voluntary staff. A full-time worker was appointed and the work flourished.

It was at this stage, in 1925, that some friends of Mrs. Kent Hughes, on returning from a visit to England, told her of the almoners' work in London and this fired her with a determination to go to London and to see for herself the work being done there. In 1927 she fulfilled her intention and spent some time in London. Of course she met Anne Cummins, who was naturally interested to hear of an enterprise, so like her own, growing out of and developing in conditions so unlike those with which she was familiar. She invited Mrs. Kent Hughes to work in St. Thomas's for some weeks so that she might see the whole organization from within and learn whatever could help her in her own work. Mrs. Kent Hughes went back to Australia quite determined that the Royal Melbourne Hospital at least—and probably all Australian hospitals—should employ almoners. As soon as she reached home, she attacked the Hospital Board. Miss Cummins had promised to choose the right almoner if the Board would sanction one. The Board was not hostile to the idea, but the Bureau of Social Service was already doing well and it was on the spot; the idea of bringing a trained professional woman all the way from England for a year to start off a really sound Almoners' Department was surely rather extravagant? And anyway, where was the money to come from? At this point Mrs. Kent Hughes displayed a certain degree of cunning. She called upon the Director of the P. and O. and, after describing the immensely valuable work being done in London by almoners, suggested that it was regrettable that Australia should lag behind in any good work and that, for a great and prosperous shipping line to offer a free passage to a woman who could so greatly enhance the value of the Melbourne Hospital was what every right-thinking Australian would expect. The P. and O. yielded, after which it was comparatively easy to get the Orient line to guarantee the return journey; it would naturally not wish to fall behind its rival line in patriotic generosity. It remained only to raise the required salary and this by her persuasive arts Mrs. Kent Hughes rapidly accomplished.

Accordingly in 1929 Agnes MacIntyre left her post as Assistant Almoner at St. Thomas's Hospital and arrived in Melbourne. Here history curiously repeated itself. As at St. Mary's Paddington a retired policeman had acted as Enquiry Officer; as at St. George's, the almoner's office was totally inadequate—it was, in fact, a bathroom! As at the Royal Free Hospital her salary was paid, not by the Hospital itself, but by outside supporters; and as in all the English hospitals she was closely supported by the Charity Organization Society. Miss MacIntyre was no stranger to the Dominion, having lived there in her youth, and she had many friends and relations within reach. It was arranged that she should stay at a guest house near Melbourne University, much frequented by lecturers and tutors, and there she was fortunate enough to become friends with Sir John MacFarland, then Vice-Chancellor of the University. Together they planned the Social Studies Diploma Course which was established later on at the University.

The work went forward with the most satisfactory speed. It was perhaps the difference of outlook between a new country and one steeped in old traditions that accounts for the fact that Dr. Cooper, Medical Superintendent of the Hospital, had in twelve months acquired an understanding of the real function of an almoner which his opposite numbers in England had not acquired in as many years. In his Annual Report of 1930 he says:

'The work of the Almoners' Department, under the charge of Miss MacIntyre, has been of extraordinary service to the Hospital. . . . The assistance given to the Medical Staff . . . has been of inestimable service to the community. . . . The Medical Staff regard this experiment as a permanency and strongly recommend its adoption in every hospital in the State.'

Agnes MacIntyre stayed for a second year in Australia and before she left was invited to Sydney to a conference with the medical men and hospital authorities of New South Wales. Thence she went on to South Australia to a meeting in Adelaide, where she had a number of medical friends who introduced her to various authorities at the different hospitals, and she was able to do much towards convincing them of the importance of medical social work. The Victorian Institute of Almoners was established and affiliated to the London Institute in 1932. Schemes were arranged for the interchange of students, as well as of qualified almoners, between England and Australia. Mrs. Kent Hughes ends her article 'During all the negotiations Miss Cummins gave us the full benefit of her help and advice. We were in close touch by correspondence, and her enthusiasm, her wisdom and deep understanding were a source of great inspiration to us all.'

This Australian venture was the last in which Anne Cummins took part. She retired from St. Thomas's in 1929. It is related by those who worked with her that at the end of a day's work, as she rose from her desk, she was wont often to murmur, 'Well, I hope I have done no one any harm today'. It was just this deep sense of responsibility, of the importance of every decision taken, together with the courage to make the decision and act on it—in spite of the real and rare humility which recognized that the decision might be mistaken—that made Anne Cummins such a remarkable worker and so inspiring to her pupils and colleagues. She had the gift of giving both freedom and support to all her workers; always enough freedom to make rather eminent almoners stay on as her assistants, feeling they had as much scope as they wished for their own work, and the chance always of hearing policy and matters of general interest discussed. And yet she was ruthless herself in urging even her best assistants to leave when there was obvious pioneer work to be done elsewhere. Perhaps her most remarkable gift was one she always said she had derived from Sir Charles Loch. She never failed to see the general in the particular. The young almoner who brought a case to her for advice soon discovered that its implications were more fundamental, more far-reaching than she had ever realized, and found her own horizons infinitely stretched.

Anne Cummins had other great gifts—an unerring sense of direction, to which Mrs. Thomas referred in her speech at the farewell dinner given to her on her retirement. This made her see St. Thomas's as part of Lambeth, and made her ready to co-operate gladly with local authorities, wishing that any good thing she had devised or received for St. Thomas's should be shared as soon and as widely as possible. She was utterly without the desire to make herself the centre of the picture or to take any personal credit for anything she achieved. It is interesting that, in reading her reports submitted to the Hospital Board or to the Northcote Trustees, while one hears much about the work, about the beneficiaries, about those who had been helpful and co-operative, one read nothing at all about the Lady Almoner, who indeed, as far as the reports go, might not exist.

It is difficult to over-estimate the debt of the profession to her, for it was she who laid its foundations; it was her strong sense, her appreciation of the essentials in every situation, her steady courageous consistency which laid these foundations so soundly that the profession was able to withstand the great difficulties already apparent when she died and the shock of the Second World War.

After her retirement Miss Cummins gave all the strength she had to the work of the Institute; her wisdom did not falter, but her strength was visibly failing. The end came swiftly as she would have chosen; there was no long illness with all the weariness and tedium it entails. She went, as the poet says, 'without a single look or a good-bye', and her friends could only rejoice that the sorrow and pain were not hers but theirs to bear.

CHAPTER XI

Emergencies and Obscurities

*'When we know their difficulties and their successes
can we wonder that the "trees" sometimes loomed larger
and seemed the more urgent problem than the "wood".'*
L. C. MARX in the *Golden Book*, 1953

The confusion about the exact function of the
almoner was perhaps inevitable in a world
changing so rapidly as it sped towards the
catastrophe of the Second World War. In 1936 the Public
Health Act was passed which laid upon local authorities
the responsibility of providing medical services for all its
citizens. The Act did not touch the independence of the
voluntary hospitals, but it made clear the intention of
Parliament that the local authorities and the voluntary
hospitals should consult and co-operate; and it empowered local authorities to make grants to the hospitals.
This co-operation was certainly necessary if an adequate
service was to be provided. For the hospitals, in a manner
so characteristic of English institutions, had developed
quite independently of one another in answer to different
needs at different times and geographically they were for
the most part concentrated in a very small area, the dis-

tricts they served overlapping in every direction. But this so obviously desirable co-operation was slow in coming; there were hesitations on both sides; the hospitals feared that by taking money from the authority they would lose some of their cherished independence, and the local authorities feared that some of the money collected from their ratepayers was likely to be spent on patients from other boroughs.

The hospitals, however, recognized that some re-organization was necessary if the nation was to be properly served and the British Hospitals Association appointed a Commission, presided over by Lord Sankey, to enquire into the situation and to make recommendations. The Sankey Commission envisaged the organization of the country into regions each containing a key hospital, which would probably be a Teaching Hospital, ruled by a Regional Commission whose duty it would be to co-ordinate all the medical services in the region.

The carrying out of this scheme was hampered by financial limitations; the King Edward VII Hospital Fund contributed to London hospitals only; and the provincial hospitals and those in Wales and Scotland were without sufficient resources. In December 1938, however, Lord Nuffield, who had financed an experimental regionalization scheme for medical services in Oxfordshire, offered to establish and endow a Trust to carry out the regionalization of provincial hospitals. The work was begun forthwith. The Regionalization Council of the Trust became its principal executive organ and since Dr. Howitt, the Chairman of the Institute of Hospital Almoners, was a member of this Council, it seemed likely that under regionalization almoners would be given their proper place and be enabled to make their distinctive contributions to the health of the nation.

Unfortunately the work of regionalization had not proceeded far before the outbreak of war blasted all hopes of a rational reconstruction. The Government determined to evacuate London and all other industrial areas and this evacuation was conceived and carried out as a military operation; the object being primarily to remove from important military centres all who would hamper military action. The point, in fact, was to get the sick, the aged and children out of the way; where they arrived and how they were accommodated was not the business of the war machine but of the Ministries of Health and Education co-operating with the appropriate local authorities.

This war did not come suddenly and unexpectedly; even the most naturally optimistic had little hope of avoiding it after Munich, there was therefore a year in which to plan the enterprise. The Ministry of Health organized the Emergency Medical Service which was to take effect immediately on the outbreak of war. It largely adopted the regionalization already being planned. To every Teaching Hospital sectors were assigned in which local hospitals were to receive patients evacuated; in these sectors base hospitals were to be established chiefly in old workhouses or mental hospitals. It is perhaps a measure of the confusion, into which the thinking about the function of almoners had fallen, that no representative of the Institute was called in by the Ministry of Health to consult about the evacuation of hospitals. For here surely was exactly the situation in which trained almoners were as indispensable as trained nurses. In fact no official use was made of these trained women. In August 1939 the Institute decided that when war came all students in training should be released to get war work. It was not easy at that moment to be sure what demands the war would make on every citizen. The Institute, however, believing that all hospitals must come to recognize the value of its work, resumed this training in the following January and appointed Miss Read to organize it throughout the country. This policy was justified, for when the call up came for women, almoners, whether fully trained or in training, were exempted from war service.

On the outbreak of war every teaching hospital became part of the Emergency Medical Service. Their first duty was to empty beds for the expected victims of bombing and the almoners were kept busy between the London and the Sector Hospitals, with the patients who had to be moved out of London still in touch with the almoner whom they knew. But while those hospitals which had long employed almoners and understood the nature of their work were able to do magnificently, softening the horrors of evacuation, the overall picture is not so happy. The upheaval was so stupendous that the plans made to meet it proved sadly inadequate. From many hospitals throughout the evacuated areas bewildered patients were discharged to thoroughly unsuitable homes; tubercular patients sent to live in overcrowded houses; schoolchildren in urgent need of treatment at a school clinic arrived at places where the right kind of clinic did not exist; expectant mothers found themselves in remote hamlets, well out of reach of the help they needed. Nor was it only the evacuated areas which suffered, the reception areas were in the same plight, for it was universally expected that London and other industrial centres would be immediately and heavily bombed and hospitals even in the sectors turned out their chronic cases and old people to make room for the expected casualties from the centre. In this general confusion the almoners did what they could. Some found themselves in base hospitals where, with everything improvised, they grappled with an immense burden of work to help out the medical staff—a staff which had mostly not the faintest idea of the real function of an almoner. All the time the administrative work increased.

Meanwhile in London a strange unnatural life went on. The hospitals were depleted, out-patient departments greatly reduced and clinics ill-attended. For the almoners, however, this meant no diminution, but rather an increase, of work. For those working in clinics could not throw off their responsibility for their patients. In many cases, especially perhaps those of the V.D. patients, who were infectious, it was all important that they should be followed up and made to attend at some centre, if out of reach of their own. The Northcote Trust workers kept the house in Royal Street open; persevered with the family clubs for those who were in London and started a club for young people to help them through the dreary black-out hours. People waited, dreading catastrophe, and nothing happened. As the weeks dragged on the evacuated Londoner began to ask herself why she had allowed herself to be lured away from the scenes she loved and the surroundings she so greatly enjoyed to a place which offered her nothing but scenery. Her hostess too, who had excusably seen herself as a noble refuge for fellow countrywomen fleeing from imminent death, began to feel almost cheated when no deaths were reported and the refugees none the less remained. For some weeks—or in some cases months—the Londoners fretted and grumbled, but before the end of the year most of them had had enough. 'Better be bombed than bored,' they said cheerfully and back they came to their familiar haunts. The out-patient departments filled up, the clinics were in demand and the almoners, working between the base and their own hospitals, had their hands more than ever full. The Institute, which in September had evacuated to Oxford, returned to London in January 1940, feeling that the work could not be carried on at a distance from the centre. In December 1939 the Ministry of Health issued a circular drawing the attention of all Emergency Medical Service Hospitals to the value of the services of an almoner in assessing the contribution which patients could be expected to make for their treatment. This, the least interesting and important part of an almoner's work, was certainly the last the profession wished to have stressed, but at least it was something to have the potential usefulness of an almoner officially recognized. Perhaps it was the Ministry circular, or perhaps it was the desperate confusion into which evacuation had plunged the countryside, which, early in 1940, brought about the increased employment of almoners. Hospital Boards which had dismissed them at the beginning of the war now reappointed them and asked for more; almoners who had drifted into other work now found themselves in demand in their own profession and returned to it.

The wishful thinking which had declared that this would be a short war was now silenced, and as the news from the Continent grew worse, the country settled down grimly to endure what must be endured for as long as it should prove necessary. London had not long to wait; in the Battle of Britain and in the nightly bombing of London and other industrial cities every part of the community was sorely tested. Few of the hospitals escaped the bombs. St. Thomas's, close beside the river and within a stone's throw of the Abbey and the Houses of Parliament—so easy and obvious a target—could hardly hope to escape. It received twelve hits and only the basement could in the end be used. Its reaction is typical of that of all the London hospitals, and in this account of the effect of the war on the profession, the experience of St. Thomas's is quoted merely because its records survive and, in addition to the reports of the almoners, those of the Northcote Trust are also available.

The bombing brought a host of new duties to the almoners. Before regular canteens were provided for the air raid shelters it was the almoners who produced hot drinks in thermoses and extra bedding for their patients, to soften the rigours of shelter nights; there were missing children to trace, advice to give on many subjects, comfort to offer in a wide variety of disasters from the complete destruction of a home with all its household goods to the loss by a widow of some forty years' standing of her 'Marriage Lines', which had made her a respectable woman for fifty years, a respectability of which Hitler had clearly no right to deprive her. Always there was the friendly cup of tea. St. Thomas's manned its almoners' department for the whole twenty-four hours and the people of Lambeth emerging at whatever hour from their devastated streets, knew that there they would find a heart-warming welcome. In fact in the London hospitals the position of the almoner as guide, philosopher and friend was fully established in the dark days of the war.

In September 1940, at the most acute stage of the blitz, a group of social workers, including Miss Roxburgh, the Secretary of the Institute, obtained permission from the Ministry of Health to cope as voluntary workers with the Rest Centres which, under the nightly bombing, had fallen into a desperate state of utter confusion. In the fortnight of the Battle of Britain they accomplished much and when that particular fury was over the Ministry, recognizing the value of the work they had done, organized a body of workers to correlate the emergency social services. In this body, popularly known as 'Mr. Willink's Young Ladies', almoners were invited to serve.

A change of heart now appeared in the Ministry of Health. A new Circular was sent in December 1940 to all hospitals. It stated:

'In the Minister's opinion, it is essential that a person who is a qualified almoner or has had experience in almoner's work should be employed in that capacity in all hospitals which admit a substantial number of Emergency Medical Service patients; in the larger hospitals it may be necessary to appoint more than one to do this work. . . . The duties which the almoner would perform are much wider than the assessment of contributions from certain classes of patients (e.g. the "transferred sick") and extend over the whole range of services which a trained or experienced almoner renders towards the social welfare and after-care of the patients. . . .'

The Circular concluded:

'I am accordingly to ask you to review the position in your hospital and to consider at once whether a qualified almoner or some suitable person who has had experience of almoner's work, should be appointed. Where a local

authority has used staff from the public assistance or any
other department purely for the assessment of contributions, it is nevertheless desirable that another officer
should be employed to perform the welfare duties indicated above.

'The Minister will recognize any reasonable amount
paid in salary as properly incurred under the Emergency
Health Scheme.'

As a logical sequence in 1942, the Institute of Almoners
was recognized under the Employment of Women
(Control of Employment) Order as an approved Employment Agency.

This Circular thus firmly and officially established the
status of the Almoner. Unfortunately a Government
Circular is not enough. Official documents are not always
read with that care and attention which they deserve,
even by those to whom they are addressed; and a popular
opinion, once adopted, is not easy to overcome. The unfortunate position in which some almoners found themselves was still the same; the majority of the general
public, including too many of their clients and not a few
of their employers, regarded them simply as part of the
administrative machine, concerned mainly with collecting
money and issuing or stamping cards. To change this
attitude was particularly difficult in war-time, since in the
chaotic conditions arising from war and evacuation it
was hard for an almoner attached to a hospital not to take
on any job that was thrust upon her. Things had to be
done. No efficient woman can well bear to see a job done
inefficiently and the worker who says disdainfully, 'That's
not *my* work,' is universally reprobated. Many almoners
therefore took on more and more clerical work, semi-

skilled work and office girl jobs, just because the things had to be done and there seemed no one else to do them. Inevitably they became absorbed in these routine tasks. Anyone who has been overworked knows that there is a moment when routine work is welcomed because the idea of tackling a problem of human relations seems beyond one's strength.

The war dragged on wearily. After the heavy bombing was over, the V bombs and the rockets resulted in spasmodic evacuations in various directions, making confusion worse confounded. Through all, the almoners struggled doggedly on, dealing with their daily problems and waiting for the day when it would be possible to embark on something better than mere improvisation.

CHAPTER XII

The Profession Established and Recognized

◆━━━◆

'The Almoner's work is an assessment of the patient's needs rather than of the patient's means.'

Report of the Royal College of Physicians, 1943

T he Second World War permitted to no one the comfortable illusion that it would be possible, once the fighting ceased, to return to normal. It was possible to endure grimly a succession of 'shelter' nights, the sound of crashing bombs, the sight of devastated cities and the destruction of homes as well as the disintegration of daily life by evacuation, but it was not possible to imagine that when all this was over there could be a return to the kind of life and to the conditions you had known before. Changes were coming in every part of the national life. It was not only the material things that had changed, ideas also had been revolutionized and those who were capable of thought realized that if they survived they would have to build a totally new world on the ruins of the old. This of course applied to all forms of social service including the health services. The whole attitude to health had changed. In the early days of the century hospitals had been regarded as a form of medical charity; they were used by those whose resources did not enable them to pay their way, and who were therefore entitled to appeal to the wealthier for relief. That conception no longer prevailed. The health of the nation was seen to be the concern of the whole people and the cost of securing it must be borne, in due proportion, by all. No one, of course, could foresee the form in which the nationalization of medicine would be established, or the rate at which it would be introduced, but that it would come was inevitable.

This being so, all who had any position of responsibility in the medical services were planning for the future and to the almoners it was a matter of crucial importance that their contribution to the health services should be recognized and accepted. Accordingly, early in 1940, the Council of the Almoners' Association appointed a subcommittee, under the wise chairmanship of Miss Edminson, to decide what steps should be taken by the Association. This sub-committee recognized that the first essential was to establish the facts about the existing situation and to this end it recommended that a research student should be financed for six months by the Association, in order that she might make a survey. Most fortunately, Miss Rees, who had been working as an almoner in Sydney, wrote in 1941 to the Association, to ask if she could be of use in England and the sub-committee saw in her the ideal research worker. She was an experienced almoner and her absence from this country during the years of stress gave her just that detachment which enabled her to see clearly things not so obvious to those who had grown accustomed to them. Her extremely valuable report, published in 1942, was circulated to all

148

members of the profession and considered at a Conference of the Association held in London in November 1942.

The Conference was very well attended and there is no doubt that it came as a shock to many of the old established almoners to discover how very widespread was the ignorance of their function displayed not only by the general public but also by many doctors and health authorities who ought to have known better. Miss Rees suggested in the survey that the immediate task before the Association was to educate the public and further that this could not be done unless the almoners' own conception of their work was clarified beyond all fear of misunderstanding.

The Conference, accepting this proposition, proceeded to a weighty discussion of the functions of an almoner. The subject had, of course, been discussed by almoners from 1905 onwards and the conclusion had always been the same, namely that an almoner is first, last and all the time a medical social worker; that her whole business is the welfare of the patient. Upon this basic definition there was complete unanimity, but on the question as to the kind of administrative work which this involved there was a division of opinion. For whereas some regarded the mere mention of administrative duties as anathema, not to be named among those who should be doing 'pure' social work, others maintained that it is not so simple to draw the frontiers between social and administrative work and that, as it is impossible to separate a man from his material circumstances in diagnosing his sickness, so it is impossible to separate him entirely from the machinery of the hospital which is treating him. Much clarification has been achieved, but to a lesser degree, this controversy continues to the present day. *Solvitur ambulando*.

The Conference proceeded to agree upon the necessity of drawing up a document setting forth the conditions under which almoners should agree to serve. This was to be submitted to all boards or authorities seeking to appoint almoners and would ensure that every employer should know what the almoner was prepared to do. Hitherto the Institute had circulated all the posts to all members of the Association, but now that the demand was far in excess of the supply it seemed right that the almoners should assert their professional status and accept posts only from such authorities as recognized it.

The Institute, no less than the Association, recognized the importance of the point at which they stood, and the immense possibilities open to the profession if the opportunity was seized. The attitude of the medical profession to the almoner had been changing steadily since the first days, when there was a tendency among doctors to regard her as a rather tiresome woman coming between them and their patients. This readiness to co-operate with the almoner was very much encouraged by the increasing realization of the truth enunciated by the eminent physician Sir Farquhar Buzzard, who was at this time President of the Institute, 'The study of disease in man cannot be made without reference to the condition in which he lives.' If this conception were generally accepted, the position of the almoner was secure, for it was precisely the study of the conditions in which each patient lived, the influence of his environment on his emotional and physical well being, that an almoner was trained to undertake. This was the foundation of the profession of an almoner which Charles Loch had first envisaged, but which had been confused and to some extent lost in the days of complete financial depression after the First World War. That this principle should be re-established and accepted was crucial, alike for the patients and for the Association and the Institute who sought to help them.

The year 1942 was an important one for it was then that the Institute received, first from the Royal College of Physicians and later from the Ministry of Health, an invitation to submit memoranda on the medical social work that should be done by almoners. The Institute gladly complied and waited to see how far its views were embodied in new legislation. The Institute itself made its declaration of faith in its Annual Report for 1942: 'An almoner's primary function is the social work that the patient's condition and treatment require, and the so-called "administrative" duties of the department will, if the primary duty be rightly interpreted, fall into their appropriate subordinate place.'

In the following year the Royal College of Physicians published a report on social and preventive medicine strongly reinforcing the almoner's view and insisting that there must no longer be any misconception of the nature of their work.

'It is hoped that in the future there will be no ambiguity about the work for which the almoner is appointed. Her association with the assessment of the means of patients and the collection of their payments to the hospital is unfortunately regarded by many people as her chief function; it is important that this misconception should be removed. The almoner's work is an assessment of the patient's needs rather than of the patient's means.'

A further most interesting suggestion was made in the report: 'The training of medical students in social medicine will offer to senior almoners a new and intensely interesting field of study and an opportunity of team work in one of the most important branches of teaching.'

Actually this was no innovation, as almoners had been giving lectures to medical students and nurses in many hospitals in an informal sort of way for many years. In Oxford there was a very important development, when Professor John Ryle, who held the new Chair of Social Medicine in the University, sought the collaboration of Miss Rees, the Head Almoner of the Radcliffe Infirmary, in the organization of Conferences with medical students to discuss cases from the Hospital. As early as 1940 at the Royal Free Hospital, the almoner who worked in the venereal disease department was asked by the medical director of the clinic to give regular lectures on the social implications of venereal disease to the medical students attached to the department. More formal teaching began there in January 1946, when the Head Almoner gave lectures to students who had completed their Second M.B. and were about to start clinical work in the Hospital; and this close collaboration has continued there ever since as in many other hospitals.

With the professional status of the almoner recognized by the highest medical authority and by the Ministry of Health; and the Institute being officially consulted by those who were planning post-war medical services, the prospects for the profession were bright and it was clear that it would expand. Naturally, therefore, the almoners looked with some anxiety at their constitution to see how far it would serve them in the strenuous days to come.

That there should be two professional bodies with an Executive Committee governing each was in itself an anomaly. In the beginning, when medical social service was a new conception, there was a justification for having a body of eminent people to preach the gospel, to find recruits for the infant profession and to direct their training. At that time the few qualified almoners were too completely occupied with their daily work to be able to survey the whole field and plan for the future, though from very early days they had met regularly to discuss the problems and possibilities of their work. Now the division—the Institute, a governing body chosen predominantly from outside the ranks of the profession; and the Association of trained Almoners, represented on the Institute, but in a permanent minority—could no longer be tolerated. The almoners had long been dissatisfied. Their Association was represented on various outside professional bodies, but had no power to commit the Institute to any course of action. This was not only galling to the representatives, but also very confusing to the public.

Discontent with the existing conditions had been increased by the war and in the difficulties and frustrations arising therefrom there was a tendency among almoners to feel that since they were not able to govern the profession all they could do was to get on with things as they were as well as possible.

Miss Rees's survey, with its disturbing revelations, strengthened the determination of the profession to set its house in order. There were discussions among almoners all over the country and between the Executive Committees of the two organizations. Agreement was not difficult, since all concerned were anxious only to establish the profession on sound lines. The Institute had been governed by an executive committee which worked through eight Regional Councils. Its great asset lay in the presence on the Councils of distinguished men and women, interested in the movement. These were leaders in the fields of medicine, education and administration; the profession had gained much from their experience and wisdom and it was most important that their interest should be retained. After much consultation a draft constitution was accepted by both Institute and Association by which the country was divided into nine regions, each governed by a Committee on which the working almoners held two-thirds of the seats. These Committees appointed representatives to the Executive Councils of the Institute in London.

The Draft Constitution for the new Institute of Almoners was accepted by both bodies at their Annual General Meetings of 1943; the legal formalities were of course slow and tedious, since that is their nature, and it was not until January 1946 that they were completed and the new Institute of Almoners represented a fully self-governing profession. It was fortunate enough to secure Professor Alan Moncrieff as its Chairman, and Sir Ernest Rock Carling later became its President, the third in a distinguished succession, Sir Alfred Howitt and Sir Farquhar Buzzard being his predecessors.

This consummation came at an opportune moment. The National Health Bill was being drafted and though in the first White Paper there was no mention of the almoner, this omission was repaired in December 1947 by the issue of a Circular dealing exclusively with her function. There was nothing very new in the definition of her work; Mary Stewart and her immediate successors would have accepted it as a description of the work they were undertaking, but what was new and most important was the tone of the document, for in it the Ministry affirmed that the almoner was a colleague of the doctor and with him responsible for the health of the patient; it stated moreover that since there were not nearly enough of these valuable women, they must be asked to do only the work for which they had been trained and be given all the secretarial and administrative help they required. Further, the Ministry indicated that almoners would be expected to play an increasingly important part in the training of medical students in social medicine and in co-operation with the medical profession on research projects in this field.

With this official recognition of its status and function, the profession may be said to have come to maturity. There have, of course, been developments of great importance since that date, but these are not the concern of this chronicle, which purports only to record, for those who are not fully aware of it, the history of the birth and establishment of a profession of which too many are still ignorant. It is no unusual thing to be asked what almoners find to do now that there is no money either to collect and little to bestow; and there are some, even in the profession, who believe that medical social work is the discovery or invention of the National Health Act. These younger members of the profession do less than justice to their predecessors who, without the official support of the medical profession, without subsidy from the tax payer, in a society which accepted poverty for the masses as a matter of course, and looked askance at 'ladies' who undertook work outside their homes, laid the foundations of the road on which they can confidently tread today.

Index